Plague Fighters

The skill of the physician shall lift up his head;
And in the sight of great men he shall be admired.
The Lord created medicines out of the earth;
And a prudent man will have no disgust at them.
Was not water made sweet with wood,
That the virtue thereof might be known?
And he gave men skill,
That they might be glorified in his marvellous works.
With them doth he heal a man,
And taketh away his pain.

ECCLESIASTICUS 38:3–7

HERMAN STYLER

~~~~~~~~~~~~~~~~~~~~~~~~~~~~~~~~~~~~~~~

Plague Fighters

~~~~~~~~~~~~~~~~~~~~~~~~~~~~~~~~~~~~~~~

Illustrated

CHILTON COMPANY — BOOK DIVISION
PUBLISHERS   PHILADELPHIA AND NEW YORK

Published in Philadelphia by Chilton Company, and simultaneously in Toronto, Canada, by Ambassador Books, Ltd. Library of Congress Catalog Card Number 60–12549. Manufactured in the United States of America by Quinn & Boden Company, Inc., Rahway, N. J.

In loving memory of my brother Harry and my young sister Emma who helped to make this a better and happier world for everyone . . . To them this book is humbly dedicated.

Foreword

". . . a flower for a loved one."

A little girl was seated at her desk in school engaged in drawing a picture. Her teacher approached and watched her quietly. At length the teacher asked the pupil: "What is it you are drawing?"

The child paused for a moment, then looked up at her and replied, "I am drawing a picture of God."

The teacher smiled. "But how do you know what God looks like?" she asked.

"Oh, that's why I am drawing it," the child replied. "I want to find out."

This little girl was creating God for herself. In like manner, we can all create God for ourselves. If man can indeed be the captain of his soul and master of his own destiny, perhaps, no matter who we are, or how lowly our station in life, we can also help to create history—and to fashion it for human betterment.

The great medical fighters in this book have done so. They were dedicated men, and many gave their lives to the tasks they undertook. No matter in how small a way, surely we too can do our share to save the lives of generations not yet born.

This is not a pleasant story, and perhaps some of it will make you angry—angry enough to want to do things about it. If it does, so much the better. That's what it did to me.

This is the story of man's ceaseless struggle against the deadly plagues of history. The battle, of course, is far from over. It is still being waged desperately on many fronts. It is forever new, forever changing, forever challenging.

This book was begun over a cup of coffee in Osborn Hall of

the New York University-Bellevue Medical Center. Here many
fighters on the medical battlefront would gather daily at lunch
to revitalize body and spirit—and try to forget about deadly
plagues for a few moments. But it was not easy.

Over delicious salads and homemade pies, we would toss
about the problems of the day and chat about delightful trivi-
alities. Thus we would find release from reality. Then, after
lunch, on a warm sunny afternoon, we would stroll over to the
Franklin D. Roosevelt Drive and gaze across the East River.
The ripples in the water sparkled in the sunshine, and the world
suddenly became full of color and comfort.

Then we would turn and walk back. A dark building would
loom before us. It was the old Municipal Lodging House on
East 25th Street, a crumbling castle of broken men. We tried
not to let it bother us, but one had to look away from it, up
into the blue sky, to enjoy the fresh air.

Soon we were back at Bellevue, with its faded red-brick walls,
washed by oceans of tears, witness to thousands of miracles.
It was visiting hour, and eager men and women scurried
through the gates. Some were clutching flowers. An old man
was selling them on the corner of First Avenue.

"A flower for a loved one," he sang.

Now and then a person would pause and buy some flowers.
They are an eloquent gesture of a simple hope. "Please get
well," they say, and they level the world. The sick will enjoy
their fragrance, and a tremulous moment of joy will come to
them. Sometimes it is the last they will know.

To help these people go on living—that is the dream of all
who fight on the medical front. That was the dream of all the
plague fighters whose story is told here. They were men of vision
and courage. Let us hope that we can do as well.

In our struggles against the deadly plagues, let us, too, find
courage and hope and inspiration. Every day medical science is
winning new victories, and soon—perhaps even in our own life-
time—the shadows at Bellevue will fade, and golden sunshine
will bathe the earth.

HERMAN STYLER

BOX SCORE OF THE GREAT PLAGUES OF HISTORY

Name	Places of Occurrence	Dates	How Transmitted	Results	Present Status
1. Bubonic plague A disease of rats (Black Death)	Swept over entire world. Started in Egypt, then swept Europe, then Asia	300 B.C. (Egypt) A.D. 1500 (Roman Empire)	Transmitted through bites of fleas infected by feeding on plague-ridden rats	Estimates of as high as 65,000,000 killed since the first recorded plague	Still occurs in unsanitary areas of the world
2. Malaria Disease of the living dead	Started in Africa, Asia, ancient Rome	Early Christian era in Europe	Transmitted by the bite of the female *Anopheles* mosquito	Approximately 200 million cases annually. Has retarded civilization in many backward areas	Sharply reduced by the WHO mosquito control crusade now under way
3. Typhoid fever A disease of filth	Ancient China, Burma, Siam, Europe, U.S.A.	Origin shrouded in mystery. Noted in Hindu records 3,000 years ago	Transmitted by contaminated water, milk, and other foods, and by human carriers	So devastating that it changed the course of human history	Effective vaccine, control of typhoid carriers, improved sewage systems—all have held it back
4. Typhus A disease of lice and filth	A fearful by-product of war, privation, and suffering	Started during the Dark Ages	Transmitted by the common "cootie"	50 million civilians and soldiers have died	Generally under control—but the story has no ending
5. Yellow fever Terror of the Tropics	Started in Africa or South America	The Middle Ages	Transmitted by *Stegomyia* mosquito (female)	Uncounted millions. Can still rise, greatly	Can be prevented, but no cure exists

6. Tuberculosis	Ancient Egypt; now everywhere	Biblical times	Transmitted by human contact	A slow killer, its effects were insidious	Effectively controlled, but still dangerous. Still rising in certain areas
7. Syphilis	Origin in dispute: Old World or New?	First appeared in Naples in 1495	Transmitted by infected humans. Can be hereditary	Many millions—not only fatalities but also serious brain damage	At least half a million a year. Still a serious problem
8. Cholera — An invisible tide of death	Originated in India, following great floods, then encircled the world	Ancient origin	Germs enter intestines, depleting body of water and minerals	Millions have succumbed. Terror existed everywhere	Still exists in many areas. Sanitation is best prevention. Antibiotics helpless against it
9. Leprosy — Disease of the untouchables	Originated in India, where the Garden of Eden "bloomed"	Ancient origin	Transmitted by direct contact. Victims have been outcasts of society	Millions since 1500 B.C. Two million in 1910	Still exists, but is slowly fading
10. Smallpox	Originated in Syria, some say. Heavy toll during Crusades and later	64 B.C.	Caused by viruses	Many millions of lives lost	Still reappears, though controlled by vaccination
11. Poliomyelitis	Perhaps Europe	Uncertain origin	Caused by viruses	Many millions killed or crippled	Salk polio shots, Cox and Sabin live-virus vaccines may conquer it
12. Influenza	Swept over Europe and U.S.A.		Caused by viruses	Many millions killed	Many types still appear

Contents

~~~ 1 ~~~

The Early Years

From earliest times plagues and epidemics have constantly wrought havoc with the human race. Ancient man could do nothing about them. He could neither fight them nor escape them. As the centuries passed, however, man began to wage a sporadic battle against them. But it was crude—and it was futile. Still men succumbed in droves, without rhyme or reason.

At last man began to make use of desperate and strange measures against these widespread catastrophes. Vile concoctions were swallowed to appease the gods; cruel tortures were inflicted upon the hapless victims. But still to no avail.

We must say this, though, for our early forebears. To fight human suffering, they did all they could and employed whatever means they had available to them. This, of course, is much more than can truly be said about modern man. Perhaps our need is not as pressing or—despite harrowing statistics—is not yet recognized as pressing. Unfortunately, however, all their efforts did our ancestors little good. They lived, they suffered, and they died.

Through trial and error, man gradually learned to profit from his errors. This was, indeed, a step forward. Surely it is a sign of mature man to admit being wrong. Though they continued to fight an unsuccessful battle not only on disease but also on grimly closed minds, the early plague fighters constantly returned to the battle with renewed effort and determination.

Finally, after centuries of failure and deep frustration, came signs of progress. Scientists began to slice through the dark clouds hovering over humanity. And soon the faint light of victory began to shine through and light up the world. When that time came, and the mysterious plagues and epidemics began at last to be recognized and conquered, surely it marked a memorable and magnificent epoch in human history.

Born of desperate necessity, nurtured through centuries of conflict, medical science too has known a stormy life. Many dramatic struggles abound in its speckled history, but the ones presented here are among the most challenging that man has waged against the microbe.

These struggles began with primitive man countless ages ago. Ancient man was a hardy creature, but he had to fight for everything he owned—and he owned almost nothing. For a long time he waged a losing battle. Archeological discoveries reveal many truths about the supposedly hardy, happy creature of the Old Stone Age. Perhaps the most basic one is this: he led a rather tough life.

Though he had no television, probably he was plagued by many of the headaches that beset our own lives. Though he had no taxes or medical bills, he was moved by his own set of joys and sorrows, broken by his own set of misfortunes.

Certainly our early forebears led a life that none of us need envy. Unable to distinguish between matter and spirit, they regarded with suspicion all things throbbing with life and emotion, and all things that they did not understand.

The tiger which chased him up a tree was certainly an ancient foe out to take his life. The tree, uprooted by a storm and blocking his woodland trail, was there to take revenge. The stone which crushed his finger was, unmistakably, possessed by an evil spirit, the agent of an avenging god whom he had innocently offended.

More formidable than this array of visible enemies was a

host of others. They were alive but invisible, and from these he had no means of escape. Like shadows in the night, they dogged him on his hunt, lay in stealthy ambush at every fork in his trail, and, in some mysterious manner, sneaked into his body and gave him the miseries.

The medicine-man was the first professional humbug of human society. Often priest of his clan, he exercised an uncanny power. Not only did he claim curative skills, but also he could just as freely invoke disease and misery upon a troublesome tribesman.

Versed in the art of witchcraft, the medicine-man effected his "cures" by the sheer audacity of his magic. If incantation and smearing of his patient with excrement failed to expel the offending spirits, he resorted to whooping and dancing, often prolonging the orgy until he foamed at the mouth and fell to the ground, exhausted. Should the patient recover from his affliction, it boomed the prestige of the medicine-man. Should he die, obviously it was the patient's own fault.

This, then, was medicine in the Stone Age. Egyptian medicine was quite a bit better. Let us take a brief glimpse at it.

On his magnificent bed of ebony and gold in the Royal Palace of Thebes, young King Tutankhamen lay gasping painfully for air. His lungs were rotting from tuberculosis, that ancient scourge of the Pharaohs. It was 1350 B.C., the end of the young monarch's short reign. The Egyptian Empire, restored by Amenophis III to its former glory, was again crumbling.

The priests of the god Amen despaired. They had been worshiping for many days before the sacred altars in the great temples, imploring Amen to spare the life of the young Pharaoh. But King Tutankhamen went from bad to worse.

Standing gravely around the King's bed, dressed in their tight-fitting panther-skin suits, their heads cleanly shaven, were the royal physicians. They had done their utmost to save the life of the young Pharaoh. But none of their remedies, despite their nasty tastes and smells, had brought relief.

"Arise and destroy the ill before thee," Zuiti, the chief phy-

The medicine-men not only claimed curative skills, but also offered just as freely to invoke disease and misery upon a troublesome enemy.

sician, is supposed to have cried, as Tutankhamen sank lower and lower. "By Isis the Divine, let the deadly germs in thy members be destroyed."

What did the King's physician mean by this reference to "deadly germs," a word now commonly used for microbes? The ancient Egyptians were reputed to have had no knowledge of the microbe. Instead, they believed that evil spirits entered their bodies and sapped away their lives.

Digging into the old ruins of Egyptian Thebes many years ago, British archeologists made a great discovery. They found a medical papyrus which they believe was written about 1500 B.C. Called the *Therapeutic Papyrus of Thebes*, this document contains probably the most extensive list of maladies and cures known to the ancient Egyptians. Still well preserved and embodying more than a hundred pages of hieroglyphic script, it was 70 feet in length and 12 inches in width. This scroll presents an amazing record of the scope of Egyptian medicine. Of little scientific value (the prescriptions are little more than fantastic dossiers of drugs, blood, and animal excrement), the document is, nevertheless, of great interest.

In addition to giving the names of many well-known herbs used by the Egyptians as drugs, it is said to describe accurately the symptoms of numerous present-day maladies.

Without thermometers to help them, Egyptian physicians relied upon their wonderful powers of observation. They noted that many physical ailments were invariably accompanied by marked changes in body temperature. Though they could not record these changes on an instrument, they could still detect them by the sensitive tips of their fingers. And that helped.

Egyptian physicians believed that disease resulted from evil spirits. Therefore, their diagnostic problem was spotting the spirit responsible for a certain disease. Wherever possible, they would search out the reason for its attack. Fortunately, the patient himself could often supply the clue by searching his memory for some past misdeed.

If a man's offense against a deity were of a petty nature,

perhaps he paid a mild penalty for his offense. Probably only a crushed arm or a broken nose. For a worse offense, a greater penalty was exacted. Or even an epidemic upon his entire community. Thus, on his dying bed, Tutankhamen presumably was paying for his father's sins.

Upon this primitive concept of disease and punishment was the fragile structure of early Egyptian medicine built.

The medical problems of the Greeks were scarcely different. It is true that they organized many branches of knowledge on a scientific basis. But they, too, were unable to extricate medicine from the enfolding arms of superstition.

The first Greek physicians placed their faith in the healing powers of Aesculapius, the mythological god of medicine. The priests administered their cures with prayers and incantations from behind the walls of temples in shaded groves. Until the time of Hippocrates, its medical practice was, basically, the same as that of the Egyptians.

The first scientific approach to medical theory was introduced by Hippocrates (460–370 B.C.). His was the first attempt at a rational interpretation of the cause of disease. Science and philosophy began to blossom in Athens at this time. It was the Age of Pericles. Euripides, Pythagoras, and Aristophanes were all alive. The thesis of divine creation had been supplanted by Aristotle's theory of spontaneous generation, and Anaxagoras had set the pace for the overthrow of the Olympian gods by new concepts of life and matter.

Surrounded by this virginal enlightenment, Hippocrates wondered how medical practice could have been so thoroughly shackled by the ignorance and the superstition of the past. How could the operation of natural laws be ignored so completely? He pleaded for rational methods in medical practice. How, he asked, could physicians still contend that diseases were caused by evil spirits and demons?

To cure his patients, Hippocrates relied primarily on the healing powers of the body, assisted by nature. He laid great stress on diet. Instead of administering large quantities of drugs, he often used wine, barley, gruel, and frequent bathing and purging. During his long and distinguished career he accurately diagnosed many diseases. In his struggle for medical progress, he survived two of the greatest plagues of his time. During one of these, Thucydides tells us, he ordered great fires built in the streets of Athens to purify the air.

Varro and Virgil, two of the most progressive citizens of the Roman Empire, also were convinced of the correctness of this procedure. Assured that epidemics were spread by bad air, Varro drained several swamps to relieve them of their stagnant waters. During the great plague, he implored the Romans to open their windows on the north side of their houses to allow the entrance of the "healthy north winds" and to close them to the "infected south winds which bred disease."

Virgil went even a step further. Some diseases, he declared, were caused by "invisible seeds which had their origin in swamplands, fly about in the air and cause infections and death—animalcules which cannot be seen with the eye and which we breathe through the nose."

With this utterance Virgil became the forerunner of the germ theory of disease, a theory which was not developed and demonstrated until many years later.

So time moved on. Kingdoms rose and fell. The crumbling of the Grecian-Roman cultures saw the complete abandonment of all that had been achieved in medicine from Hippocrates to Galen, the foremost physicians of the early era. With the advent of the Dark Ages, medical practice once more fell under the domination of priests and quacks.

Once again disease and epidemics became the products of spirits and devils, the heavenly bodies, and the wrath of Jehovah. Not until some 15 centuries later did a few physicians and scientists begin a revival of the spirit of science.

∾∾ 2 ∾∾

Shadow of the Microbe

It was Louis Pasteur, the French scientist, who burst open the medical floodgates in 1854. His was the first practical discovery in man's effort to unmask the offending microbe. It came as a result of a number of wonderful coincidences.

A research chemist and school teacher, Pasteur became the Dean of the Faculty of Sciences at the University of Lille. Before coming to Lille, Pasteur had conducted a series of experiments with the fermentation of liquids to test the theory of spontaneous generation. At Lille, he decided to continue his experiments. Perhaps he remembered the sound prophecy of Robert Boyle, the chemist, who, more than two centuries before, had predicted that an understanding of fermentation would furnish the key to the cause of disease.

Pasteur worked tirelessly in his small attic laboratory at night, hoping to complete the investigation. One day, while absorbed in his researches, he was approached by a representative of Lille's hard-pressed businessmen.

"We are calling on you," the visitor said, "to ask if you would investigate a serious problem in connection with our wine and beer industry."

Pasteur straightened up and listened. For a number of years

Louis Pasteur

this important industry had been steadily disintegrating. Now it had taken an alarming turn. No one, least of all the brewers, knew exactly what was wrong. Nor could anyone suggest a remedy. The producers of beer and wine suffered staggering reverses. Millions of francs were being lost. Many producers had already gone bankrupt.

The liquor in some of the great vats simply would not turn to alcohol. It promptly turned sour.

After hearing the story, Pasteur offered his help. On visiting the local distillery, he noticed that some of the vats containing the liquor were covered with froth and had a pleasant odor. He took some of this foam in a glass tube, sniffed at it and corked the tube. Then he examined other vats. Where there should have been a similar bubbling foam there was, instead, a sickly, grayish scum with a foul odor. He took some of this scum in a separate flask, and, making no promises, departed.

Back at his laboratory, Pasteur placed a drop of the scum from the second tube on a clean slide and looked again. This time he saw a striking difference. Instead of lively yeast globules, great numbers of little animals came into view. They were wormlike, squirming organisms, propelling themselves freely about in the liquid. He squinted and looked again, hardly believing his eyes.

"They are microbes!" he exclaimed. "These are the little beasts that cause the spoilage of liquor!"

The great chemist was excited. He was sure that he had found the answer. After a while he quieted down—and then the question hit him. How could he destroy the microbes without spoiling the quality of the wine, the good French wine? With characteristic zeal, Pasteur accepted it as a personal challenge.

He had discovered the cause, and now he would attempt to find a remedy. He began by experimenting with antiseptic substances. These antiseptics readily destroyed the organisms, but they also spoiled the flavor of the wine. Then he decided to try heat. So he heated liquor to various temperatures. At last, at 55° Centigrade, all the microbes in the liquor were killed without impairing the quality of the wine.

Pasteur's patience, his microscope, and an abundant faith in science thus came to the rescue of a vital French industry and preserved their tantalizing wines for posterity. More significantly, it opened the gates to exciting pathways of medical progress. But the physicians of his time were not ready to follow.

After this success, Pasteur resumed his work with fermentation. But again he was interrupted. An emergency call came from the leaders of another dying French industry. A mysterious disease was attacking the silkworms in southern France.

Where once they grew fat on the leaves of the mulberry trees, the silkworms now refused to eat. They would not even spin the cocoons from which their precious silk threads could be unwound. Strange little brown spots appeared on their bodies; they sickened and died by the millions. Disaster threatened the French silk trade unless a solution could be found— and quickly.

The silkworm experts were at the end of their rope. They made all kinds of wild moves, but the silkworms continued to die. French silk became more and more scarce. Once again, in its hour of need, France turned to Pasteur.

"The chemist, Monsieur Pasteur, the chemist," they cried. "Let's send for the chemist! Perhaps he can help us."

But, as in all human endeavors, there were skeptics, still suspicious of a mere scientist.

"What does Pasteur know about silkworms?" they scoffed. "He is only a chemist. He might know about fermentations, but what does he know about silkworms?"

Nevertheless, they sent for the chemist. And the chemist came willingly. Pasteur knew nothing about silkworms, it is true, but he knew the possibilities of his cherished microscope.

Even more, Pasteur had faith in himself. And not without cause.

So Pasteur went to the silkworm district in southern France.

There he selected several of the insects and examined them under his microscope. In the pulverized bodies of some of the worms he saw vast numbers of tiny specks which he knew should not be there. He further noticed that when eggs which contained these brown spots hatched, the worms were sickly and usually died, while healthy eggs produced healthy silk-worms. The connection between these foreign spots and the disease flashed in his mind.

"They're microbes," he told the silk producers. "They multiply in the bodies of the silkworms. This disease is inherited through diseased eggs from one generation to another. Eliminate the diseased eggs and you will produce healthy crops of silkworms."

The farmers accepted his advice, selected uninfected eggs, and saved their industry.

Pasteur now embarked on another untrodden pathway. Could skin diseases be due to the action of microbes? Perhaps, he reasoned, these invisible animals in the air and the water were even responsible for the putrefaction of flesh and the decomposition of organic matter. Though not a trained physician, he immediately decided on a series of experiments to test the validity of this theory.

Scarcely had he begun the work when urgent calls for help from other fields forced him to abandon it. He had become a national hero, and his advice and services were now being desperately sought throughout all of France.

While Pasteur himself was unable to carry out his projected line of research, his work aroused widespread debate among scientists. But the medical men, jealous of his intrusion into their field, refused to take him seriously. "Pasteur is only a chemist," they snorted, "and what does a chemist know about disease?"

Yet, at that very moment, many brilliant strides were being made in medical progress.

3

The Plague Fighters
Move Up

The health of man during the early nineteenth century presented a dark picture, indeed. In both Europe and America cholera and typhoid posed major problems. Frequent outbreaks of diphtheria and typhus occurred, and there was almost no help, almost no surcease from sorrow. Many bacterial maladies attacked European and American cities. In the Orient people succumbed by the millions.

Anesthesia had come to the aid of surgery—in Massachusetts General Hospital in 1847—but the number of deaths from infection and blood poisoning was still large. Patients went under the knife with their chances of escaping death well below 50 per cent.

In the maternity wards of European and American hospitals, childbed fever spread like wildfire. In London, Vienna, Paris, Philadelphia, and Rome the story was the same. The disease would suddenly break out and spread from ward to ward, often killing as many as 60 per cent of the mothers. Between 1750 and 1800 numerous major epidemics of puerperal fever broke out in European maternity hospitals. In 1831, it has been re-

13

ported, of 31,950 babies born in the maternity wards in Paris, 25,000 died. In a single year in Dublin, out of 10,250 births, only 45 children survived.

So the dark clouds grew darker. The cries of the living deadened the sound of death.

Then at last in 1847 came help. A young Hungarian doctor named Ignaz Philipp Semmelweis came upon the scene. Working in a maternity ward in Vienna, Semmelweis saw mothers die by the hundreds. The horrible sights in the morgue sickened him. What was the use of medical science, he asked, if it made no effort to save the lives of these helpless creatures? Haunted by the specter of death stealing through the wards, shocked by the agony and the screams of the frightened mothers, he would retire bitterly to his room at night. Torn by anguish, he could not sleep. The rattle of death followed him everywhere.

"The wards are nothing more than murder chambers," he wrote to a friend in Budapest, "and the horrible conditions in them evoke not the slightest sentiment in the hearts of the medical authorities."

Somewhere in the hospital, Semmelweis contended, the disease must have its origin. From there it must spread through the wards. Urging new methods in the handling of patients, he advocated that only doctors and medical students with clean hands be permitted to examine mothers.

The maternity hospital in Vienna was organized into two divisions. Medical students in the first division attended women in childbirth and performed postmortems on childbed fever victims. In the second division, women trained as midwives attended mothers in childbirth. Unlike the medical students, they did not come into contact with the deceased.

Semmelweis observed that in the second division ward the death rate was half the first. Students and physicians must sterilize their hands before they attended living patients, he pleaded. And his voice was finally heard.

The results were truly amazing. Previously, from 200 to 250 out of every 1,000 women who were operated on had died. During the following three months the death rate declined to

12 out of every 1,000. The rate of the first division fell below that of the second division. During a two-month period no deaths at all occurred in the first division.

Thus did Semmelweis lead the way in our long battle against infection. Unfortunately, this great doctor himself died of an infection in Vienna before his work was finished.

Scarcely ten years later, Joseph Lister, an Edinburgh physician, was likewise pleading for immediate reforms in surgery. Surgical methods were unsanitary, and this encouraged disease if it did not actually breed it. Lister, too, had seen doctors examine patients without properly washing their hands after autopsies. Before performing operations, they would don their evil-smelling frock coats, frayed at the cuffs and splotched with blood stains. From this practice, Lister reasoned, might be found a partial answer to the age-old question: What is the cause of infection and disease?

To Lister it was exceedingly clear. If Pasteur's theory was correct—that invisible organisms in the air were the cause of fermentation of liquids—what was to prevent such organisms from causing putrefaction in flesh wounds?

While operating, Lister decided to use carbolic acid as an antiseptic. At first he applied it to the bandage, but later, by means of a new instrument, he sprayed it on the wound. While he operated or dressed a wound, the air about him was constantly sprayed with it to destroy the microbes. His instruments, when not in use, were kept in the solution to keep them sterile.

The success which followed this technique was phenomenal. His results spoke so eloquently for Pasteur's theory that today they seem to be quite obvious. But to the doctors of Lister's time any innovation was highly suspicious. Unwilling to acknowledge the validity of a theory that they were unable to discredit, they resorted to persecution and boycott.

"Lister is an upstart," they snorted, "pitting his whimsical visions against the accumulated wisdom of the great authorities. Anyway, who knows whether there are any germs in the air to begin with?"

But Lister held his ground. When he went to London to

demonstrate his new principles, he found himself confronted by a stone wall of opposition. It came from both the medical profession and the church. They had even organized the nurses and the nuns for a boycott of this new "medical folly," as they chose to call it, and accused Lister of violating the Lord's Day because he changed a soiled dressing on a Sunday. Yet nothing could shake Lister. On February 19, 1874, he wrote this simple tribute to Pasteur:

Please allow me to take this opportunity to render you my most cordial thanks for having by your brilliant researches demonstrated to me the truth of the germ theory of putrefaction, and thus furnished me with the principle on which alone the antiseptic system can be carried out.

The germ theory of disease, amply demonstrated by Pasteur and Lister, was finally accepted. The analogy between air and microbes, between disease and putrefaction was clearly established. However, there remained one significant question to be answered. Were *all* microbes producers of disease? Or did specific types of microbes produce specific types of disease?

As early as 1546, Fracastorius, the celebrated physician of Verona, had published a startling treatise on disease and contagion. Living, invisible organisms, he had declared, are able to cause disease. Contagion is spread from one person to another by direct or *indirect* contact.

Years later the idea was further expanded. In 1762 an Austrian, Anton von Plenciz, presented strong arguments to support his belief that living agents were the cause of communicable disease. He had even ventured to suggest that a specific microbe probably existed for each disease. Nobody, alas, picked up the idea.

But the search went on desperately. In 1840, Jakob Henle, the pathologist, published an essay in support of von Plenciz. Like his predecessor, he could offer no supportable evidence to bolster his suspicions, though he searched diligently for what he termed "microscopic forms" in contagious material.

It was then that Robert Koch, a country doctor, appeared on

In 1546, Fracastorius declared that living, invisible organisms are able to cause disease.

the horizon. Intrigued by the little animals that he saw swimming about in his new microscope, he began a systematic study of them. In 1876, on close examination, he recognized the anthrax bacillus, a microbe long suspected as the cause of a serious disease in sheep.

Now one victory crowded upon the heels of another. A year later, from Berlin, Koch announced one of his greatest scientific triumphs: the discovery and the isolation in pure culture of the tubercle bacillus, the cause of tuberculosis in man. His success with the anthrax and the tubercle bacilli furnished conclusive proof that specific diseases were caused by specific microbes.

More important still, it brought full confirmation—even medical recognition—to the germ theory of disease.

The decade 1875–1885 was an exceedingly fruitful period for medical science. A spectacular line of discoveries in the field of bacteriology, regarded until then as a minor branch of science, followed.

We know now that different species of organisms produce different diseases, and that some microbes are not at all harmful—only neutral. Some are beneficial, while many are indeed necessary for the vital processes of life.

Thus we can see that a most minute idea, developed with persistence, can alter the course of human history. That man could shape his destiny, in a tremulous moment of discovery, is to his eternal credit. Men of talent and dedication were always necessary, of course, but happily we had such men—and so we advanced.

$\infty\infty$ 4 $\infty\infty$

The Microbe in Action

If you never have seen a living microbe under the lenses of a microscope, a real thrill awaits you. It is like visiting the zoo for the first time and then feeding the elephants. Seeing a microbe for the first time is such an unforgettable experience, awesome and wondrous.

It is quite easy to see the microbe. If a microscope is unavailable, a good magnifying glass will afford an interesting spectacle. Pour a few spoonfuls of water into a shallow glass dish. Then add a bit of grass or a few pebbles. Leave the dish on the window sill for several days for a film to collect.

If you examine a drop of this film you will be amazed at its activity. A single drop will contain a considerable number of paramecia, among the simplest of all animals. Under the microscope they resemble chunky, twisted cigars. Their bodies are surrounded by minute hairlets, called cilia. On one side, in the body wall, is a slight depression, or oval groove. Sometimes paramecia live in colonies, in an intimate group. Sometimes they live and function independently. The other common protozoan, the ameba, is frequently referred to as amebae or proteus animalcule. Though most of them cannot be seen with the naked eye, they are animals nevertheless.

19

Like animated jelly, the ameba can change their shape at will. They constantly throw out irregular threads of extension. Often the shape of the ameba is not unlike a drop of thick liquid which has fallen and spattered. It consists of an inner granular mass and an envelope of somewhat clear substance. The nucleus, which is a large spherical globule inside the interior granules, consists of a clear substance.

Possibly the most fascinating part of these little creatures is their constant movement. It seems likely that their energetic contortions are a ceaseless search for food. As soon as an ameba comes in contact with an edible particle, it enfolds it, the particle sinking into its body, where it is digested and assimilated.

If you keep your eyes glued to the microscope long enough, you will see a birth take place. As do all living things, the protozoa, too, must reproduce. The first indication will be a constriction at a point where the nucleus will be divided. This goes on until the animal resembles a dumbbell. Then the lobes separate, and each becomes a distinct and complete whole. In time, each of these will undergo a similar division, the multiplication going on indefinitely.

Microbes increase at an exceedingly rapid rate, multiplying by a process called binary fission. One cell splits into two, each a complete individual, the whole process taking only a few minutes. At this rate one microbe can turn into a vast army in 24 hours. In the case of many pathogenic organisms this multiplication rate militates against the germs themselves. Injurious substances are released which inhibit their reproduction and cause self-destruction.

Even the ameba observe the laws of self-preservation and have learned to protect themselves. Two Johns Hopkins University professors, L. C. Busch and S. O. Most, in a series of experiments, found that these minute forms are able to learn by experience. They learned to shun heat and bright light by the trial-and-error method as they moved about in a drop of water.

They do this by means of feelers, or pseudopodia. When these feelers strike a region of warmth or light, they are promptly withdrawn. But they do not back away. Instead, they project other pseudopodia in another direction. If they fail to find the right spot, they continue "feeling" until they encounter conditions that are suitable for survival. Then they move on.

In order to fight an enemy, we must know as much about it as we can. We must know its habits, its character, and its purpose in living. There are many species of germs—many good, many evil. Without germs, life would be impossible, because many devour each other. Imagine the world with millions of dead animals scattered about and no microscopic life to decompose them!

Man can number among his benefactors a host of microbes. They are extensively used in the manufacture of a number of foodstuffs. In the dairy field one species is used in the souring of milk. Different varieties of cheese owe their distinctive flavor to the microbes which accelerate their ripening. Microbes are also necessary in the production of vinegar, beer, and cider. They change slush and sugar into alcohol, convert sugar into lactic acid, and are widely used in the organic chemicals which process textiles.

Though they require nitrogen for growth and development, many important plants are not equipped to utilize it. They must have it in the form of nodules attached to their roots. So they depend on the "nitrogen fixer" microbes. These absorb the free nitrogen of the air and change it into nitrogenous compounds which the plants—clover, alfalfa, and other legumes—utilize to enrich the soil.

Strange as it seems, dynamos can be run by bacteria. By their chemical action, huge amounts of energy can be released and used for industrial purposes. Under suitable conditions, when light is excluded and the temperature averages about 100° Centigrade, certain bacteria are employed to convert sludge and sawdust slush into acetic acid. They are, in addition, used in the production of methane gas, a valuable source of heat.

When, in 1916, the Allied blockade prevented Germany from importing fats for the manufacture of glucose for ammunition, German chemists tried to develop a substitute. Within a year they had not only found this substance, prepared by means of micro-yeast, but also were producing it in large quantities. Thus, for the first time in history, man brought the microbe directly into war.

Athanasius Kircher (1602–1680), the pathologist who examined the blood of victims of plague, is often credited as the first person to have seen the microbe. However, his feat is discounted by many scientists. It so happens that the cadavers autopsied by Kircher were victims of plague. The disease is caused by the microbe *Bacillus pestis*, so tiny that it is far beyond the range of visibility of any microscope in use in the seventeenth century. Kircher's microscope gave only a 32-fold magnification. It is generally believed now that what Kircher saw were merely red blood cells.

As far as supportable evidence is concerned, Antony van Leeuwenhoek, a Dutchman, was the first person to have seen the microbe (1676). The organisms which he saw were the paramecium and the ameba, both found in nearly all bodies of water and frequently in the air.

Van Leeuwenhoek was not a scientist, nor was he searching for the microbe. A drapery maker by profession, he ground lenses and built microscopes as a hobby. Fortunately, he was not content with merely making microscopes—he wanted to see things, too.

Thus it happened, one day, that Van Leeuwenhoek placed a drop of rain water under his microscope. He saw strange animals swimming about under his lenses. Delighted by what he saw, he called his daughter out of the house to look too. This was truly the first time that human eyes had ever seen the microbe!

Wild speculation ensued. People traveled miles to take a peek at this marvelous instrument. Imagine, the invisible became visible! Small things became large! Before long, the news reached the Royal Society in London, the most distinguished scientific body of the time. It appointed one of its members to check on rain water. This microscopist, Robert Hooke, made his own microscope and peered into the water. And there, exactly as the Dutchman had said, were living creatures before his eyes!

The story of the little animals in the microscope spread far and wide. Everyone in the countryside talked about them. But they were not important enough to be dignified with scientific classification. They were simply called "little beasts," or "animalcules," names given to them by their discoverer, Van Leeuwenhoek. In 1758, almost a hundred years after they were first seen, the zoologist Carl van Linnaeus termed them *Chao*. This was an apt name in view of the chaos created by previous attempts to classify them. In 1763, Wrisberg gave the first scientific name to the whole kingdom of microscopic creatures. He called them *infusoria*.

In 1829, another scientist, Ehrenberg, came to the conclusion that the term *infusoria* was inadequate. It made no distinction between the microbes that resembled plants and those that resembled animals. So he went a step further. He grouped all those which resembled plants into one division to which he gave the name *bacterium*.

The word "bacterium" comes from the Greek and means staff or rod. The word probably appealed to Ehrenberg because most of the *infusoria* he was investigating at the time were rod-shaped. So bacterium became accepted. It is from this term that the whole science of bacteriology has taken its name.

Some years later, in 1854, the eminent scientist, Ferdinand Cohn, took yet another step forward. He pointed out that, since the class of organisms named bacteria by Ehrenberg had a closer resemblance to the lowest forms of plant life—such as the algae—than they had to animals, they properly belonged to the plant kingdom. Therefore, he declared, they should be part of the science of botany.

People are often confused by the complex terminology of biology. So perhaps a few things can be cleared up here. The word that is frequently used today in referring to the whole kingdom of microscopic life is *microbe*. It has the identical meaning that the word *infusoria* had before 1829.

"Bacteria" continues to designate but one single class of microbe. But they are not the same. The word "germ" is employed rather loosely to mean a harmful organism. Today, however, even the word "microbe" is rapidly giving way to *microorganism*, and germ killers have become antibiotics.

Let us gaze into the microscope again. When we examine stained material which contains more than one species of organism, we can see that each displays its individual shape and arrangement. Some are oval, some spherical, and some grouped together in clusters. Several even resemble chains.

Upon these intriguing variations in shapes and arrangements, scientists have based their subdivisions of microbial classifications. Organisms which are rod-shaped are called *bacilli*; those which are spherical or bead-shaped are the *cocci*; finally, the spiral-shaped are called the *spirilla*.

The coccus or bead-shaped group, it was observed, assumed three distinct arrangements. Therefore, a separate term was applied to each. In some cases the organisms are always seen in a cluster formation, resembling a bunch of grapes. To this arrangement the name staphylococcus (staph for short) was given. The straight and single ones, like individual beads on a string, are called streptococcus (strep). When arranged in pairs, they are called diplococcus.

The earlier system of naming microbes was an ingenious one. Scientists joined the type of microbe and the disease it produced into one name. The name of its discoverer followed in parentheses. Thus, *Bacillus typhosus (Eberth)* indicated that the microbe was a bacillus; the disease it produced was typhoid fever; and the discoverer of the microbe was Eberth. Now take *Diplococcus gonorrhoeae (Neisseria)*. This indicated a diplococcus arrangement of the microbe, gonorrhea the disease it produced, and Neisser the man who discovered it.

While it gave three important facts at once, this system was cumbersome. Therefore, it was modified by eliminating one of the words and directly adding the name of the discoverer. As, for example, *Eberthella typhosa*, or *Neisseria gonorrhoeae*.

All species of microbes have been grouped roughly into three main divisions—protozoa, the bacteria, and the viruses. Each division in turn has been broken down into various subdivisions. The protozoa are recognized by their resemblance to simple animal life; the bacteria, the largest division, by their likeness to the simplest plant life; the third group, the viruses, still cannot be classified so easily.

Thus far, only a few of the viruses have been seen. They are usually too small to be detected with even the most powerful microscope. Viruses are so much smaller than bacteria that a pin's head, which can accommodate 100,000 bacteria, could accommodate a half million viruses.

Certain microbial phenomena which baffled their discoverers have remained a mystery years later. One such phenomenon is the water of the Ganges River, in India. Many infected natives, in religious ecstasy, wash themselves in the Ganges even during an epidemic. For a long time Westerners wondered how those who drank this water managed to survive. Some even attributed curative properties to the river.

Back in 1896, M. E. Hankin became curious about this. He collected samples of water from different parts of the river and subjected them to rigid microscopic tests. But he could find nothing. There was only one conclusion—the water of the Ganges had germ-killing, or bactericidal, properties.

Was it possible that the viruses had destroyed the bacteria? This mystery was further deepened when it was shown that the water retained its bactericidal properties after filtration but lost it after boiling. Nothing further was heard of all this for the next 20 years.

Then, during World War I, Felix d'Herelle, a French bacteriologist, came upon the scene. He was preparing vaccines to be injected into patients suffering from typhoid fever and amebic dysentery. At the same time, he injected animals with cultures of these microbes, believing that, in some way, the disease could be conveyed to these animals. Thus he would be able to study the bacilli in live tissues.

M. d'Herelle first prepared his filtrate from the stool of a dysentery patient. Then he put it in an incubator to await injection into the animals the following day. Under normal conditions, after 12 hours, the filtrate would have turned cloudy from the rapid multiplication of the germs. But, to his astonishment, instead of a cloudy suspension, it became a clear liquid. He centrifuged the liquid, but no sediment collected at the bottom of his test tubes.

Here was a phenomenon which would have electrified Pasteur. What had happened to the bacteria in the liquid? There could be only one answer: bacteria cannibals. The dysentery microbes had been devoured by the other invisible organisms which somehow had escaped the lens of the microscope! To confirm this, he prepared a second culture exactly as he had prepared the first. To it he added a few drops of the clear liquid from the first tube and again incubated it.

The result was identical! After making enough of these tests, d'Herelle formulated this theory of what probably happens: There are cannibal microbes, invisible, yet able to destroy other microbes—destroy them so completely that no trace of them remains. The discovery of these bacteria destroyers, called a bacteriophage, is extremely important. If a bacteriophage destroys bacteria in suspension, why not employ them to destroy microbes in human tissues? D'Herelle had solved the riddle of the Ganges and opened new vistas for medicine.

Without our present ingenious methods, we would know little of the activities of the microbe. Without our most wonderful instrument, the microscope, we might still be unaware of the world of invisible life. Today our compound microscopes are instruments of phenomenal precision. The microscope, with magnifying powers up to several thousand dimensions, enabling scientists to pry into worlds undreamed of, has indeed become man's greatest ally in his ceaseless battle against the microbe.

Now that we have seen the enemy—its face, its figure, and some of its disguises—perhaps we can proceed on clearer ground.

~~~ 5 ~~~

The Pale Horseman *

The heavy, black smoke curled leisurely skyward as the ship steamed toward San Francisco. It was a day in March 1900. It had been a long voyage from the Orient, and everyone on board was tired. But there was to be no landing. A passenger had come down with bubonic plague, and news of it had caused panic on the ship.

But for the foresight of several alert physicians, San Francisco would have found itself in the grip of a plague epidemic. Knowing its fearful record, they took prompt action to isolate the case and thereafter to scrutinize all incoming ships from the Orient. As a result, no other plague case appeared in San Francisco that year nor during the next two years.

In 1903, however, the microbes succeeded in eluding American plague detectives. Another outbreak occurred in San Francisco, attacking 121 people, of whom 113 died. In 1907, still another outbreak in that beautiful city took 78 of 186 victims it attacked. During this period minor occurrences were also reported in Oakland and in Seattle, but these were arrested before the infection had a chance to spread.

Although man has always been plagued by this dread disease, it was not until 1894 that the *Pasteurella pestis* was identified

* The Pale Horseman was the name used in referring to bubonic plague. The origin of the term is vague.

27

as its cause. Alexandre Yersin, a pupil of Louis Pasteur's, and Shibasáburo Kitasato, a pupil of Robert Koch's, both working independently, isolated the organism in pure culture during the great plague of Hong Kong.

For a long time it had been suspected that rats brought on the plague. However, the exact nature of this relationship was unknown until 1907. In that year Captain W. Glen Liston, a member of the Indian Plague Commission, demonstrated to an astonished world that the disease is carried to rats by fleas. In a remarkable experiment, he showed that caged rats suspended beyond reach of plague-infected fleas did not contract the disease. Other rats, left within reach of the fleas, soon contracted the plague and died.

Little is known of the history of bubonic plague before the fifth century, B.C. No one knows positively what types of epidemic afflicted the Babylonians or the Persians, the Medes or the Assyrians. These people, like primitive races before them, regarded epidemics as tokens of the displeasure of their deities, just as the early Christians accepted them as manifestations of the wrath of Jehovah.

The early Hebrews, too, regarded the plague and other epidemics as divine retribution. In the Book of Deuteronomy (28:21-22) Moses charged the Levites to warn the people against disobeying the commandments that God had given to them: "The Lord shall make the pestilence cleave unto thee, until he have consumed thee from off the land, whither thou goest to possess it. The Lord shall smite thee with a consumption, and with a fever, and with an inflammation, and with an extreme burning. . . ." But the Israelites disregarded this threat, and this type of punishment was measured out to them. "Thus they provoked him to anger with their invention, and the plague brake in upon them" (Psalm 106:29).

"And Moses said unto Aaron, Take a censer, and put fire therein from off the altar, and put on incense, and go quickly unto the congregation, and make atonement for them: for there is wrath gone out from the Lord; the plague is begun" (Numbers 16:46). Aaron did as Moses directed and "stood between the dead and the living; and the plague was stayed. Now they that died in the plague were fourteen thousand and seven hundred" (Numbers 16:48–49).

During their 40 years of wandering in the wilderness, the Israelites suffered repeated visitations of disease. Most of them, from their violent nature, indicated bubonic plague. Following a lapse into idolatry, 24,000 died from a plague (Numbers 25:9). During a military expedition against the Midianites, the officers failed to carry out the commands of God, given to them through Moses; people whom they should have killed were brought back as captives. Since the Israelites had been led to worship Peor, the Moabite god of uncleanness, again God had sent a plague as punishment (Numbers 31:16); and Moses and Eleazer the priest caused many of these captives to be slaughtered as retribution.

Since the wilderness country afforded such a meager supply of food for such a great multitude, the Bible relates that a heaven-sent food, manna, was provided each morning; it was white "and the taste of it was like wafers made with honey" (Exodus 16:31). "And the people went about, and gathered it, and ground it in mills, or beat it in a mortar, and baked it in pans, and made cakes of it: and the taste of it was as the taste of fresh oil" (Numbers 11:8), that is, cakes baked with oil. However, nourishing as it was, some of the Israelites recalled their diet in Egypt and demanded meat. Although God was angered by this discontent, yet he answered their request by sending great flocks of quail "from the sea, and let them fall by the camp," and the people easily captured the birds. But "while the flesh was yet between their teeth, ere it was chewed, the wrath of the Lord was kindled against the people, and the Lord smote the people with a great plague" (Numbers 11:31, 33).

Many years later, at the height of the reign of King David, a great plague was brought upon the Israelites as punishment for the King's transgression in taking a census of his subjects. "So the Lord sent a pestilence upon Israel from the morning even to the time appointed: and there died of the people from

Dan to Beersheba seventy thousand men" (2 Samuel 24:15).

The destruction of the army of Sennacherib, king of Assyria, who had laid siege to Jerusalem, may have been a sudden outbreak of plague; 185,000 men died in one night, and Sennacherib quickly retreated to his own land (2 Kings 19:35–36).

Such is the evidence of the pale horseman among the ancient Hebrews.

The ancient Greeks, too, had their share of bubonic plague. It began in 430 B.C. as a result of the rivalry between Sparta and Athens, the two most powerful Greek states. By then the Athenian Empire had extended westward as far as Sicily and eastward to Asia Minor. It had achieved a democratic civilization which, in the words of Colton, the British scientist, "was nearly two grades higher than our own."

In contrast with this enlightened democracy, Sparta was headed by a rich and powerful landed aristocracy. The Spartans held the intellectual flowering of Athens in contempt. War soon broke out between Corinth, ally of Sparta, and Corcyra, ally of Athens. Athens thereupon came to the aid of Corcyra, and Sparta declared war on Athens.

Anticipating the strategy of the Spartan attack, Pericles, the famous Athenian leader, prepared his defenses accordingly. He brought the entire population of Attica into the city, confident that its impregnable walls would withstand the enemy's pressure. Since a powerful Athenian fleet controlled the sea lanes, an ample food supply, he reasoned, could always be brought in.

Under the command of King Archidamis, the Spartans marched into Attica. As Pericles had anticipated, their plan was to devastate the fields. The Athenians, they hoped, realizing that their source of food supply was being systematically destroyed, would abandon their defensive positions behind the city walls and come out into the open to fight.

What actually happened was much worse. Athens simply could not accommodate the entire population of Attica. With a normal population of over 450,000, the city was now more than doubly taxed with every available space occupied.

People crowded the public buildings and every emergency shack that could be provided. Worse still was the food problem. The strong fleet upon which Pericles had counted to deliver a continuous food supply was being harassed by pirates. After a few months, many necessities of life were unobtainable. Added to all this was the problem of cleanliness. The Ionian capital, despite its remarkable scientific and democratic achievements, was without adequate sanitation.

According to Thucydides, the historian of the Peloponnesian War, the plague began in Ethiopia. Then it invaded Egypt and Libya and was carried by sea to Piraeus, the seaport of Athens. There it spread rapidly through the populace. Thousands fell dead in the streets or plunged headlong into the watering places to quench their burning thirst.

The rapidity with which men caught the infection was amazing. As the plague raged, Athens became paralyzed. In their great distress, the devout begged mercy of the long-forsaken Olympian gods.

Learning of the havoc within the city, the Spartans hastily withdrew. However, they returned the following spring, and the siege continued. For several years the plague slackened and flared up intermittently. At last the once glorious city of Athens was forced to its knees. The Golden Age of Pericles came to an end.

With all its nobility of spirit, her art and her science, the first great experimental democracy was no match for bubonic plague.

The first recorded epidemic of the Christian era occurred during the reign of Marcus Aurelius. Called the plague of Antoninus, it struck terror into the heart of the Roman Empire.

Marcus Aurelius was considered a peace-loving scholar. Unfortunately, he became emperor at a time his people were facing their most pressing danger. Marcus inherited barbarian enemies and a legacy of aggression from Trajan, Hadrian, and Antoninus Pius. In the East, the Parthian King, Vologesus, had risen in revolt. He had defeated the Roman army guarding

Syria and had occupied Antioch. It was a tremendous blow to Roman prestige.

The victory was due not so much to enemy strength as to Roman weakness. Guarding Syria, with headquarters at Antioch, soldiers and officers alike wallowed in lust and debauchery. They caroused in the cypress groves of Daphne where, as Monroe said, "they skipped nothing." Gambling, drinking, and lewd parties so softened them up that they were woefully inadequate to meet the Parthian attack.

To rescue Roman prestige, Marcus Aurelius dispatched two of his ablest generals, Varus and Cassius, to recapture Syria. Varus proved to be vulnerable to the lures of Syria, but Cassius was made of sterner stuff. Reorganizing the army, he succeeded in driving the enemy out of Antioch and most of Syria.

Scarcely had the soldiers begun to celebrate their victory on the banks of the Tigris when the plague broke out. The entire army was smitten. Within seven days over 40,000 men were dead. Thousands more lay helpless along the banks of the river. The fury of the plague finally abated, but the returning soldiers carried the disease germs with them to Rome.

Hardly did they embrace their wives and sweethearts when the epidemic flared again. The Holy City was thrown into consternation. People died so fast that burial could not be provided. Entire families were wiped out in a single day. Corpses lay everywhere, blocking the streets. Carts carrying the dead to be heaped into pits were blocked by bodies at every turn.

The pestilence lasted 15 years, abating and reappearing at intervals. It nearly ruined Italy. The Roman army was virtually wiped out, and the time was now ripe for its downfall.

Toward the middle of the sixth century A.D., the old Empire collapsed. In Rome, Theodoric I ruled as the first Gothic king, his kingdom extending across the Alps and down the Adriatic to Dalmatia and Serbia. The Ostrogoths ruled Italy with an iron fist, with Justinian, the Lawgiver, as sovereign ruler of the Eastern Empire. For a while it showed signs of a vigorous revival, but a series of new disasters soon sealed its fate.

The first was an earthquake which in two minutes made rubble of Antioch. It leveled three fourths of the city, killing and maiming over 200,000 persons. On the heels of this came a great Italian earthquake, then drought and famine.

Constantinople was almost completely depopulated. The death rate in this city alone for the first three weeks of the plague period was 10,000 daily. As with all plagues, it did not discriminate, and even the mighty Justinian and the officers of his government fell. Thus the once mighty Roman Empire finally came to an end.

Man is indeed a hardy creature, and the overwhelming need to survive is certainly one of the attributes of the human race. How else can we account for the fact that, despite the stupendous forces lined up against him, man did survive, gather new strength, and eventually overcome many of his destroyers?

Commonly known as the Black Death,* the plague of 1347 which devastated most of Europe and parts of Asia has been called the worst epidemic that the world has ever known. It was a pestilence of inconceivable fury and severity, surpassing in its range and destructiveness all other plagues before it.

Brought from the Orient in the late summer of 1347, the epidemic struck Europe with the fury of a tidal wave. By the spring of 1348, it had visited Sweden, France, Spain, Florence, and London. In less than 24 months, it prostrated most of the large cities of the Continent and laid low parts of Russia, the Scandinavian countries, Ireland, and the Netherlands.

Adding fuel to the spreading flames was the pilgrimage to Rome. The year 1348 was a Holy Year. To induce Christians to undertake the journey to Rome, Pope Clement VI offered advance absolution to all who might die on the way. Their souls, he promised, would not be delayed on earth but would gain immediate entrance into heaven.

Thus encouraged, the pilgrims set forth from all parts of plague-ridden Europe and Asia, spreading the disease wherever

* The name Black Death is derived from the dark hemorrhages which appeared beneath the skin around the eyes of its victims.

The great plague of 1347, commonly known as the Black Death, devastated most of Europe.

they went. By Easter, 1348, over 1,250,000 of them had visited Rome. Ten per cent of these lived to return to their homes. The rest, let us hope, went to heaven.

The epidemic, Hecker estimated, took more than 25 million lives. Guy de Chauliac, the able physician of Clement VI, who survived the disaster, declared:

It covered the whole world, or lacked little of doing so. It was so great that it left scarcely a fourth part of the people. I say its like has never been heard of before. Of the pestilences in the past, none was so great as this. Those could be treated in some way, this in none.

In this connection, Oliver Wendell Holmes made a sage comment, "The United States has been singularly fortunate," he told a class of Harvard medical students, "not to have been a geographical part of the European Continent either during the present century or any other century since or before the Christian era."

Today, however, this is no longer true. Let us hope that in our smaller world we shall have a greater opportunity for help and co-operation, that we shall have greater power to *save* lives rather than *take* them.

∞ **6** ∞

Destiny Takes a Hand

In an isolated camp in the White Mountains of New Hampshire, several hundred men lived dangerously through the first year of World War II. They were not fighters, but they contributed immeasurably to victory.

These men were conscientious objectors, and they became subjects of an interesting and vital experiment. Army doctors were making typhus tests, and these men had volunteered to prove that they were not disloyal citizens.

One hundred were selected to play the grim role of guinea pigs in a pioneering project. The object was to find a more efficient way to control typhus.

The determination of the Surgeon General to prevent an outbreak of typhus fever was no mere routine. It was based upon a real dread of this silent enemy which had chalked up such a fearful record in previous conflicts.

"Typhus fever," Colonel Edgar Erskine Hume reminded the College of Physicians in Philadelphia in March 1942, "ranks first as a wholesale man-killer. . . . Every army has had to fight this invisible foe. It is the evil companion of privation and suffering. Down through the ages comes the tale of its ravages. . . ."

36

The common body louse, or "cootie," is one of the most effective fifth columnists ever to confront an army. It has spread typhus among millions of soldiers and civilians during every major disaster, whether famine, earthquake, or war. Where sanitary facilities are inadequate, typhus fever gains an easy foothold. It follows the soldier into trenches, barracks, and hospitals, and wreaks havoc on the men. So the army doctors in New Hampshire worked painstakingly to find a way to conquer it.

One hundred uninfected cooties were released on each volunteer. The men were instructed not to kill any of the bugs and to refrain from scratching themselves. They were not to remove any of the insects from their bodies or interfere with the insects in any way.

The insect "guests" quickly dug in. They established themselves in the seams of shirts, pants, and underwear. Within a few days every volunteer became infested. The multiplication rate of the cooties was so rapid that within a month every man had upon his person an average of 1,000 insects.

The question now was, how could the bugs be killed without hurting the men? Actually, there was a product which could do just this. But there were complications.

A gas known as methyl bromide had been used with good results. Created after extensive research by the Bureau of Entomology and Plants, the Food and Drug Administration and the Rockefeller Foundation, it had been found by tests to surpass every known weapon used against the body louse. But how could cylinders of gas be used in the foxholes? Therefore, the army had to find individualized protection of the soldier without gas tanks and delousing stations.

Even before the war, the Government had been in possession of a valuable vaccine. Developed in 1938 by Dr. Harold Cox of the United States Public Health Service, it had proved to be effective. When injected in time, it prevented the development of typhus fever. But this vaccine could not be made in sufficient quantities to meet the demands of the armed forces. The only recourse was to find a way to deal directly with the body louse before typhus fever broke out.

The compound DDT was found to be a powerful agent against certain species of insects. It was also known to possess a high potency against cooties. Within 30 minutes after direct contact with the powder, the insects would begin to tremble, fall into nervous paroxysms and wither in 3 hours. Applying this chemical to bugs under controlled conditions was one thing. Dusting it under the clothing of soldiers was quite another. The army's immediate problem was to discover such a method yet not affect the skin or respiratory system of the soldiers.

For months the doctors toiled. The cooties crawled with ecstatic abandon. How were they to be killed? The dilemma was finally solved by combining DDT powder with other chemicals. One of these compounds did the trick. When dusted onto the underclothing of the men, no skin injury or impairment of the respiratory system was observed. The compound could be produced in almost any desired quantities, quickly and cheaply. After a year, the men were scrubbed up and sent home, their mission completed.

Not a moment too soon. The experiments were finished just in time to save a section of the American Army in Europe from what could have been a major disaster.

Forty persons every week were falling from typhus in Naples in the spring of 1944. With the American Fifth Army destined for this theater of operations, the outlook was fraught with danger. Several months before our troops entered the city, a grand dusting party took place. Everybody was dusted off. Delousing stations were set up everywhere. All houses, caves, tunnels, and transport vehicles were sprayed with the DDT compound. After that few succumbed. Thus the American Army saved Naples from a possible typhus fever scourge.

Although the body louse, *Pediculus corporis*, is the principal agent in the transmission of typhus fever, the direct cause of the disease is the microbe *Rickettsia prowazeki*.

The insect acquires the microbe by biting a typhus patient, sucking up blood containing the parasites. The germs soon multiply in the insect, discharging numerous microbes into the bite. From here they work their way into the tissues where they reproduce rapidly.

However, all typhus infections do not start this way. The disease can be acquired by simple contact with an open wound, or by crushing the louse and rubbing its infected blood or feces into the skin. The louse alone can hardly spread an epidemic. When spread by personal contact, however, typhus fever can reach epidemic proportions.

The onset of the disease is marked by alternate chills and fever followed by a rash. The temperature rises rapidly, with chills, depressions, weakness, and pains in the head and the limbs. First appearing as pink spots which fade on pressure, the eruption soon becomes purple, then brownish red, and finally brown. Typhus is easily recognized by this combination of a rash, fever, and delirium.

The research in this field was intensive. In 1909, Dr. Howard Ricketts, examining the blood of persons afflicted with Rocky Mountain spotted fever, identified a group of organisms which were subsequently named after him. These were: *Rickettsia rickettsii*, the cause of Rocky Mountain spotted fever; *Rickettsia quintana*, the cause of trench fever; and *Rickettsia prowazeki*, associated with typhus fever. In the midst of his investigations, Dr. Ricketts himself contracted Rocky Mountain spotted fever and died.

The rickettsiae have attributes of both the ordinary bacteria and the viruses. Yet they are neither. Many bacteriologists prefer to regard them as intermediate between these two forms. The rickettsiae are sometimes found in chipmunks, ground squirrels, gophers and rabbits, in the tick and the mite, and, of course, in our old enemy, the common body louse.

It may seem strange that the etiology of typhus fever was not worked out until recently. The answer is that for a long time typhus was confused with plague, typhoid fever, and cholera. Fracastorius, in 1546, gave it a clinical description and called it "spotted fever," noting that it was accompanied by severe thirst, delirium, and eruptions of small spots on the skin.

About a year after Fracastorius' description, Jerome Cardan, an erratic but clever physician, also mentioned certain peculiarities of typhus fever. Annoyed by the medical follies of his time, Cardan decided to write an exposé—perhaps the first in history. It was called *The Bad Practices in Modern Medicine in Common Use*. Though fragmentary, the book was hailed as a brilliant piece of work.

In addition to incurring the wrath of physicians, certain passages in the book offended the Pope. The physicians boycotted him out of practice, and the Pope commanded him to throw away his pen. Thereafter, poor Cardan found himself neither a practicing physician nor a writer.

Among other things, Cardan described typhus as "flea-bite disease." Not that he thought fleas were responsible for typhus fever, but merely that the spots on the victims' bodies resembled flea bites. The real cause of the disease, he believed, was the presence of "foreign substances" in the blood.

Over 350 years elapsed before another step was made toward solving the mystery of typhus fever. In 1909, Charles Jules Henri Nicolle, Director of the Pasteur Institute, made a study of the malady among poor typhus patients in Tunis. After lengthy investigation, he declared that typhus fever was caused by the bites of infected body lice.

It is a curious fact that the course of typhus fever has paralleled that of bubonic plague. However, typhus has been somewhat less violent and is chiefly a disease of cold weather, whereas the plague flourishes best in hot weather. But if bubonic plague was the terror of early wars, typhus fever has been equally dreaded in later conflicts.

Typhus has been known by a variety of names. One was "jail fever," derived from the frequency of its attacks on penal institutions where sanitation was mostly nonexistent. Others were "spotted fever," the disease of the early mariner. During the siege of Granada, when it killed thousands, it was named "tabardillo," due to the mantlelike nature of the rashes which appeared on the victims' bodies.

Unlike the plague, typhus has had a comparatively short, if

The carrier.

terrible, history. In 1097, almost in the wake of a devastating
famine which swept southern Europe, the first Crusade was
organized. The Crusaders, an immense army of fanatical Christians bent upon wresting the Holy Land from the Turks, came
from a dozen countries. First they crossed the Bosporus and
captured Mecca. Then they embarked along the identical route
which Alexander the Great had followed centuries earlier, on
his way to Antioch. After besieging the city for nine months,
the Crusaders finally captured it.

Part of their army remained in the fallen city, but a smaller
force, under Godfrey of Bouillon, plunged forward to capture
Jerusalem. The looting, the slaughter, and the pillaging which
followed have no equal in history. Not satisfied with mere
plunder and murder, the Crusaders set torches to the cities.
The result was ruin. A typhus epidemic, finding fertile soil in
the resulting squalor and human misery, broke out immediately.

The havoc was frightful, but destiny again took a hand. As
though in retribution, the fever attacked the Crusaders themselves, putting an end to their lust. With hands clasped tightly
in prayer, they sought the protection of the holy sepulchers,
but it was no use. Conquerors and conquered alike keeled over.
Before the fury of the epidemic subsided, the two cities were
virtually wiped out. Of the 300,000 Crusaders who started out,
only 60,000 lived to return.

In 1157 another great typhus epidemic broke out. This time
it occurred in Rome among Frederick Barbarossa's soldiers. Before the disease ran its course, two thirds of them had died—
and thousands of Roman citizens went with them. In 1544, it
struck the Hungarian army of 30,000 men, under the command
of Joachim II Hektor of Brandenburg. While attempting to
capture Budapest from the Turks, virtually the whole army was
destroyed, and the small number who remained alive fled in
terror.

That's the pattern of the story over and over again. There
seemed to be a perpetual contest to see whether man could
destroy himself faster than the microbe could. In the long and
costly struggle between Charles V of Spain and Francis I of

France for supremacy of Italy, there occurred a twin epidemic which finally ended the conflict in favor of the Spanish monarch. In all its terrible history one thing, at least, could be said in favor of the microbe; it did more to stop wars than statesmen did.

In 1528, the armies of Charles V, under the command of the Prince of Orange, were stationed in Naples. Ill-clothed, undernourished, and worn out by fighting, they were soon mowed down by a typhus epidemic. Learning of the predicament of his adversary, Francis I decided to capitalize on their misfortune. He sent a powerful army of 25,000 men to capture Naples. His men had scarcely taken up their positions around the city when a second outbreak occurred. This time, though, it attacked the French, killing off 21,000 men.

Wartime epidemics are difficult to control. Sanitation is generally broken down or reaches its lowest ebb through the usual easing up of health regulations. Contagious bacilli from an infected person might easily find their way into a brook or a well and pollute an entire drinking system.

A few individuals freely mingling with others in limited quarters can easily spread contagion. Contaminated food and water, severe hardships, general malnutrition, and lack of proper medical care are also contributing factors.

In the trenches typhus is started by infected lice. A prisoner or even an officer or a refugee arriving at one front from another might unknowingly carry such insects with him and start the disease on a second front. There is no end to the ways in which an infectious disease might spread when conditions are favorable.

The greatest typhus outbreak of all time occurred during the Thirty Years' War. It accounted for over half a million lives! Typhus also took an astonishingly large toll during the War of Polish Succession (1733–35) and created havoc with the Russian, the Swedish, the French, and the Austrian armies during their Seven Years' War against Prussia and England (1755–63). The estimated typhus loss was more than twice the number of men who died in battle.

Napoleon, too, became involved with typhus. In 1806, after he was refused the hand of a Russian princess, he organized his Grand Army of more than half a million men and invaded Russia. Shortly after their arrival in Lithuania, things began to happen. In July, they fought the battle of Ostrowk, with heavy losses. Thirty thousand men were seriously wounded. Living in cramped quarters, with poor food, water, and sanitation, more than half succumbed to typhus within two weeks. With the disease cropping up constantly, the main army reached Moscow in the middle of September. Instead of finding food and warmth in the Russian capital, as they had anticipated, they found it quite hot. The city was in flames, with desolation everywhere. No longer did they have to fight the Russians. They had a more sinister enemy on their hands.

When the retreat from Moscow was ordered on October 19, 1806, fewer than 75,000 men were fit for duty. A woebegone remnant of the Grand Army of France, it was barely able to walk. When they reached Smolensk, fewer than 40,000 remained alive. By the time Vilna hove into sight, it had dwindled to 20,000 men. The others perished along the way, their half-starved, frozen bodies forming grotesque black crosses in the gleaming snow.

The story of typhus has no ending. Fifty millions have suffered agonies and met a miserable death from it. And who knows how many million more will die of it? Fifty million people—a round, hollow figure! It is sometimes hard to think of them as human beings who lived and loved and died and were lost forever, disappearing with their unborn children down the drainpool of time. Lives never to be heard of again, except in the pages of a book, where they are put down with care.

How, indeed, does this figure affect us now? It is a lifeless figure, almost without meaning, with no joy or sorrow left in it. But it once represented bright human dreams—dreams now shiny, metallic sticks of type. Dreams transformed into black ink and splattered on a brand-new page. That is all that is left of them now . . . tiny figures on a white page.

But these figures are not really without meaning. They pound into us like a sledge hammer. What can we do about them? How can we stop such catastrophes from ever happening again? These are questions that must be answered. They must be answered by an overwhelming and determined effort by men of good will everywhere. We must wipe the bloody slate clean. Those of us who live for a better tomorrow, a tomorrow of decency and dignity for all, and are willing to fight for it, will surely know the joy and the richness of living the good life.

7

On the Trail of
Typhoid Mary

On a wet, dismal afternoon in November 1938, a Department of Health ambulance rolled through the gate of Saint Raymond's Cemetery in the Bronx. Two men lowered a metal casket into an open grave and hurried away. The casket contained the body of a woman whose name had become a classic symbol of medical frustration. Typhoid Mary she was called, the greatest microbe carrier in history.

As she had been in life, unbefriended and unwanted, so Mary Mallon remained in death. No one came to mourn her passing. No one followed her to her final resting place. She was a woman without a friend.

The damage that Mary did to humanity was enormous. How many she sent to their graves or infected with typhoid fever will never be known. A tragic emotional problem was involved here. Feeling that she was the object of unmerited persecution, Mary Mallon steadfastly refused to co-operate with health authorities. She refused, to her death, to give any information about her past.

As a cook, "Typhoid Mary" Mallon unknowingly infected hundreds before she was discovered to be a carrier.

Mary's sinister role as an unsuspecting public enemy was unearthed in 1906 by the epidemiologist, Dr. George A. Soper. A skilled investigator, he tracked her down relentlessly through a series of typhoid outbreaks. These occurred in places as far apart as Tuxedo, Sands Point, Mamaroneck, Oyster Bay, New York, and Dark Harbor, Maine.

Mary Mallon was a cook. In handling food, she innocently transferred the typhoid bacillus to hundreds of summer guests in these towns. Her gallbladder was a living culture tube. Unaware of this curse which nature had so unwittingly placed upon her, she passed the disease germs about most generously.

When Mary's case was first brought to light, typhoid fever was far more common than it is today. It appeared in many American cities, sometimes attacking scores at a time. In 1909, the death rate from typhoid was 35 out of every 100,000 population. In New York State, in 1907, close to 1,500 reported cases were recorded. In New York City four persons died of the disease every day.

While it was known that typhoid germs were disseminated through water, milk, and many foods, scientists were greatly puzzled. Mysterious outbreaks occurred in small villages, in isolated farmhouses, in palatial country dwellings, and in mountain resorts—where no known primary cases of the disease had been known to exist. In these places instances of polluted water, milk, and food could hardly have occurred.

That human beings could act as disseminators of pathogenic microbes had long been suspected. Park and Beebe, in New York, and Robert Koch, in Berlin, had suggested this possibility in 1892. Reed, Vaughan and Shakespeare, after their investigations, had warned that persons who had recovered from typhoid fever, cholera, and diphtheria might, for a long time thereafter, carry and excrete the specific poisons of these diseases. Such persons were a real source of danger. But how could an outbreak of typhoid fever be explained in a mountain resort where the water had been tested and food obtained from a locality where no typhoid existed?

Tracking down Mary Mallon was an arduous task. She

baffled the experts for a long time. Her arrest and subsequent imprisonment came through an outbreak of typhoid in the home of a wealthy Oyster Bay family. There were 11 people in the family. One day 7 were suddenly stricken with a violent seizure of the disease. Despite intensive investigation, no clue to its origin could be found. But the researchers had overlooked the possibility of the human carrier. However, the last searcher on the case did not overlook a thing. He was our friend, Dr. Soper.

Suspecting this unexplored human factor, he carefully scrutinized all persons who had come in contact with the stricken family. The last examined were the servants. Each was questioned until Dr. Soper came to the cook. But where was she? All he could learn was that the cook had left shortly after the outbreak. Worse yet, her whereabouts were unknown. This was enough for Dr. Soper. From that moment on Mary Mallon was a hunted woman.

Like a good detective, Dr. Soper studied all angles. Through an employment agency where Mary had obtained jobs, he was able to develop new leads. He found that she had worked for eight other families, and he immediately made the rounds. At each stop, except one, he found that typhoid fever had broken out among members of the household shortly after Mary's arrival. Yet, in no instance, had the cook ever been suspected.

It was a grim search with many lives at stake. Weary with fatigue, Dr. Soper never relaxed his vigilance. But Mary was always a step ahead of him. Finally, when he caught up with her, she fought like a tigress. She had no intention of admitting her guilt, of which she was completely unaware. She refused to co-operate. She knew nothing about typhoid fever. Never had she had the disease and never had she produced it in others. They were hounding her for nothing, she wailed.

To all outward appearances, Mary was right. But the evidence against her was too strong. Cultures made daily of her urine and stools, forcibly taken, proved to be positive in every case. There was no doubt about it. Somewhere in her gallbladder the germs of typhoid fever had found a happy life.

They multiplied within her and passed off through her urine and feces. Since she often handled food with unclean fingers, she thus passed on the germs to countless innocent people.

As a public safety measure, Mary was forced to become a privileged guest of the city. Such a proved potential menace could not be allowed to continue to roam at large, spreading typhoid fever wherever she cooked. She was given a comfortable little cottage on North Brother Island in the East River, where she lived and ate alone. Even her food was brought to her.

On Christmas morning, 1932, a man went to deliver a package. Receiving no answer to his knock, he peeked through a window and discovered Mary was lying on the floor of her cabin, paralyzed from a stroke. She was moved to the Riverside Hospital and was confined to bed for a number of years. On the morning of November 18, 1938, after a disastrous career as an innocent killer, Mary Mallon died.

Newspapers carried Mary's story throughout the world. She was the most famous microbe carrier who ever lived. But several other cases were equally tragic. One of these was that of a Mrs. Legree of Hanford, California, reported in the *Journal of the American Medical Association* in October 1914. In a single day, Mrs. Legree sent 93 people to the hospital with typhoid fever and three of them to their graves. It was a bumper crop. She had infected them by helping in the preparation of a church dinner attended by 150 people.

One may reasonably ask at this point, "What of the microbe carrier himself? Doesn't a carrier also get the disease?" Not necessarily. A carrier is a person who may not have had the disease but harbors its bacilli. Though protected against the ailment through an inherent or acquired immunity, he is still able to infect others. The more common carriers harbor the diphtheria, the typhoid, or the cholera bacilli.

Ordinarily, the carrier is a seemingly well person. He gives no indication of his infectivity and frequently is not aware of it. But he carries the germs in his gallbladder or intestines, where they multiply freely and are thrown off through bodily discharges.

There are two kinds of carriers: the temporary and the permanent (or chronic) carrier. The temporary carrier is a person who has recovered but entertains the germs of his disease for weeks—even months—thereafter. Eventually, however, all the germs disappear. The permanent carrier is doomed by the continuous presence of the microbes in his body. He has no way of ridding himself of these unwelcome guests except, sometimes, by removal of his gallbladder. Mary Mallon and Mrs. Legree were permanent carriers.

It is quite obvious that unknown carriers constitute a great hazard to public health. Yet what can be done about these unfortunate people? Can every man, woman, and child in the United States be checked to find those who are potentially dangerous? It would be an endless task.

Various attempts have been made to estimate the number of possible carriers of pathogenic microbes, but nothing conclusive has been achieved. Among others, Anderson, Goldberg, and Hatchel have made a study of 4,000 cases in Detroit and found that 2 per cent harbored virulent diphtheria microbes. In New York State some 400 known typhoid carriers are now under supervision. This simply means they are not allowed to work in restaurants or other public places.

Probably we shall never be able to trace typhoid fever to its first appearance. It is quite possible that it was one of the earliest diseases to plague the human race. Considering its power of infectivity, its means of transmission, and the lack of early sanitation, it was undoubtedly one of the common human scourges.

Described in Hindu records over 3,000 years ago, typhoid fever ranks as one of the major diseases of the East. It appeared long ago in China, Burma, and Siam. Until the time of the American occupation, when sanitary measures and a health control program were introduced, typhoid killed 20 out of every 100 Filipinos. Outbreaks were frequent in ancient Egypt

and were known in Carthage and Nineveh. Typhoid fever
plagued the Chaldeans too. Alexander the Great, on a visit to
Babylon, contracted it there and died.

In Persia, too, during the reign of Artaxerxes, a severe typhoid
outbreak occurred. The distressed Persian monarch, it is reported, sent emissaries with costly gifts to Athens, imploring
Hippocrates to come to Persia to help his people. Hippocrates
is said to have declined on the grounds that his physical condition could not withstand the journey.

Though many ancients knew that typhoid fever was in some
way related to polluted drinking water, they could go no further. Hippocrates recognized typhoid fever as a disease distinct
from amebic dysentery.

During the Franco-Prussian war these two diseases accounted
for 60 per cent of all deaths in the German Army. In each
year of the American Civil War 10,000 out of every 100,000
men were stricken with typhoid.

During the Spanish-American War, instead of our gaining
on the typhoid microbe, it gained on us. Of every 100,000 men
admitted into the army, 14,000 died of the disease. In the Boer
War the death rate was still high: 100 men out of every 1,000
died. Then suddenly came a change. In World War I, only 5
men out of every 100,000 died of typhoid!

What had happened? The answer lies in advanced medical
knowledge, improved sanitary conditions, and, no less important, in the development and the use of a typhoid vaccine.

The use of a typhoid vaccine, consisting of killed typhoid
bacilli, was suggested in 1896 by Sir Almoth Wright, a British
physician. It was used experimentally in the British Army in
India in 1898 and among the British troops in the Boer War.
Like many other new ideas, it met with staunch opposition.
By 1911, however, the United States Army had begun inocu-
lating its forces against typhoid, and by 1917 the entire United
States Army and Navy had been inoculated against typhoid.

Most people today know that typhoid bacilli are spread by
means of milk, food, and water. This has been demonstrated

again and again by our bacteriologists. The obvious solution, therefore, was the pasteurization of our milk to eliminate this danger. Fortunately, almost all public milk supplies today are pasteurized—one of the great gifts of Louis Pasteur to mankind.

Danger is always lurking in such foods as clams and oysters because they sometimes subsist on poisoned food. This danger may be reduced by adequate cooking to kill any pathogenic organisms. But a far better way is avoidance of shellfish taken from polluted waters.

The margin of infection from vegetables and fruit is slim; nonetheless it exists. This leaves water as the most important source of infection—water that has been polluted by human excreta.

As far back as 1856, when typhoid aroused wild concern, an English physician, Dr. William Budd, came up with an idea. He suggested that impure water seemed to be the source of at least two typhoid outbreaks. Dr. Budd observed that typhoid epidemics frequently occurred only among people who drank from a certain place, usually a well. In an adjoining community, where people obtained their water from another well, no one developed typhoid. These factors seemed to be logical enough to him. But how could he prove them to others?

Almost half a century passed before Dr. Budd's suspicions were confirmed. Now we know that the germs of typhoid fever usually enter water by way of sewers. Through surface water, which has come in contact with fecal matter containing the microbe, they can be washed into any watershed. This was a very frequent cause of early typhoid outbreaks.

Seldom does infection come from a well-guarded public water supply system, the gravest danger lying in wells supplied by surface drainage or contaminated by carriers, and in brooks and streams.

The common idea that a running brook is safe because its impurities have been removed is untrue. No water is safe to drink unless it is free of pathogenic organisms. And pathogenic organisms have frequently been found in clear running brooks.

Here is how this happens. The seepage from a privy reaches

a nearby open or underground stream. If that privy is used by
a typhoid patient or carrier, the stream will contain the bacilli.
When it bubbles above ground, despite its apparent purity, it
is nothing less than a shot of poison.

This is exactly what happened in New York in the spring
of 1939. Three boys were on a hiking trip in the suburbs. After
their water canteen was empty, they became very thirsty so
they started in search of drinking water. A mile away they
came upon a stream which oozed out of a little spring. It
looked cool and refreshing. Without any thought of its source,
they drank avidly.

More than a week later two of the boys came down with
typhoid fever. Examination of the water by health authorities
showed that the spring from which they had drunk was the
source of infection. Microbes from a distant cabin had reached
it through fecal matter.

There are scores of other ways through which these invisible
enemies can accidentally reach man.

A strange error caused a scare in New York. In 1947, three
cases of typhoid fever were discovered in Washington Heights.
After following many leads, health inspectors were stymied—
they could not find the source of the infection. Finally, a clue
was furnished by the victims themselves. Questioning revealed
that all had purchased fruit from a certain store.

Inspectors and public health nurses leaped into action, and
in a little while they were on the trail. Through the store ran
the sewer and water pipes supplying the building. Down the
sewer pipe, around which fruit was stacked, coursed an almost
unnoticeable trickle of water which reached some of the fruit.
But that was enough. The trickle was charged with typhoid
bacilli. A known microbe carrier had been living on the third
floor of the same building.

How could such a thing happen?

It was the same building—but it had a different address. The
building stood on a corner. The fruit stand faced the street,
while the entrance to the building was on the avenue. Hence
they had two different addresses and no one realized that there

were two addresses for the one building. However, a gray-haired public health nurse played a hunch on a fantastic coincidence and cleared up the mystery.

Normally, all American cities are supplied with safe drinking water. New York City has, perhaps, one of the most efficient and best water supply systems in the world. The city has spent millions of dollars to bring good water to its population and is spending millions more to keep it safe. In spite of all sanitary precautions, however, deadly microbes might still reach a reservoir or a watershed. Therefore, every effort is made to destroy them by means of filtration and chlorination before the bacilli reach the kitchen tap.

Curiously, inspectors who test our drinking water for the presence of typhoid and other dangerous pathogens do not search for these organisms. That would be a waste of time. They search, instead, for an indicator. This indicator is another group of microbes, the coliform bacilli (of which *E. coli* is one) which are constant inhabitants of the intestinal tract of man, and are thrown off through body excrements. If a given amount of water contains too many of these germs which are, under normal circumstances, harmless in themselves, then the water is considered unsafe. Since it is so highly polluted with the coliform bacilli, typhoid bacilli could also be present. Such a watershed would then be closed "for repairs."

Remembering the great European and early American outbreaks of typhoid fever and cholera which were traced to water supplies, New York State made the earliest attempt in the United States to give to its citizens pure water by building a purification and filtration plant in Poughkeepsie in 1870. Today there are over 700 of these rapid filter type plants in use in the United States—constantly on guard against a Typhoid Mary.

Now, through dedicated personnel and intensive co-operative effort, typhoid fever is gradually on its way out. Let us hope, as the years roll on, that never again will a Typhoid Mary appear on our horizon.

8

Napoleon's Prize Contest

In the summer of 1807, after many days of misery, a four-year-old French boy died of strangulation in the arms of his mother. This death ordinarily would have gone unnoticed in medical history. In this case, however, it touched off a fabulous contest that was to engage the interest of almost every physician in Europe. For the boy was the favorite nephew of the Emperor Napoleon.

In those days it was not uncommon for children to succumb in this manner. Countless thousands had fallen victim in Europe, Asia, and America. The medical profession could do nothing to save their lives or even to alleviate their suffering.

When a messenger reached his headquarters in East Prussia with the news, Napoleon was visibly shaken. For a long time he stood motionless, gazing at the message clutched between his trembling fingers. When he finally lifted his head, he had conceived a plan of action. It was not to be a military campaign but a medical crusade. He would enlist the medical profession in a total war against this strangler of children.

When the messenger returned to Paris two days later, he was armed with a bristling directive from Napoleon. A prize contest was to be launched immediately that would throttle this enemy of children. The competition was to be open to every physician in Europe, with an award of 12,000 francs to the winner.

Though it did not directly bring about a cure for diphtheria, Napoleon's prize contest partly accomplished its purpose, for it fostered an intensive study of throat diseases. Lured by medical fame and the sum of 12,000 francs, frock-coated medicos inked up their quills and wrote copiously on what they knew about what was generally called croup. Though most of what was written would now be dumped into the wastebasket, it was not all wasted effort.

Eighty papers were submitted. After five years' study, the judges found two papers to be of exceptional merit. These were submitted by J. A. Albers, of Bremen, and Louis Jurine, of Switzerland, both well-known physicians, and the 12,000 francs were divided between them.

Briefly, Jurine argued that the croup was a catarrh, coming from the mucous membrane of the larynx and the trachea. He believed that the disease was derived from such climatic conditions as cold, heat, and humidity. However, he failed to indicate exactly how these "climatic conditions" affected the body.

Albers, the other prize winner, said that the croup was an "inflammation of the mucous membrane of the larynx, trachea, bronchi . . . and partial to children." Like Jurine, he declared that the illness was the result of "climatic influences acting on a catarrhal condition," and devoted most of his paper to the stages of development of the affliction.

This, in effect, represented the most advanced medical knowledge of diphtheria in 1815.

Despite its antiquity, there is no available record of diphtheria epidemics before the sixteenth century A.D. Yet, no doubt, numerous outbreaks occurred. The first of these, according to Baillou, struck France in 1576, afflicting many thousands, of whom "great multitudes died piteously."

Spain followed France in the number of outbreaks after 1576. From 1583 to 1620 a series of them swept the Spanish peninsula at frequent intervals, quieting down during the following decade but flaring up again in 1630 and occurring regularly thereafter.

In 1618, while Spain was still in the throes of a second epidemic, the pestilence invaded Italy, where 8,000 persons, most of them children, died in Naples. During the next 20 years Italy experienced no fewer than five major visitations. Germany, Sweden, and England soon followed. By 1800, virtually every European country and many large American cities had been visited by this pestilence, wiping out hundreds of thousands of lives. Diphtheria had joined the ranks of the world's great killers. As late as 1878 a diphtheria epidemic killed over 2,000 per million in London.

The seeds of research sown by Napoleon's contest did not fall on barren ground. Besides inspiring numerous articles in medical journals, the contest aroused the medical profession and profoundly influenced the future of a resourceful, if eccentric, young French physician, Pierre Bretonneau.

Bretonneau had already distinguished himself in private practice. His ability and initiative brought him to the attention of the medical authorities of the hospital at Tours, where he was invited to become staff physician. Intrigued by Napoleon's contest, he made a careful study of all the papers published on croup.

At Tours, he was soon given an opportunity to see things for himself. In 1818, the Legion of La Vendéi arrived in Tours and was quartered in barracks recently vacated by other regiments. Though no sign of infection in the ranks of the departing soldiers had been visible, the Legion was scarcely unpacked when scores came down with the croup. Within a few weeks the plague was out of hand. It spread with disastrous results among the people of Tours, overcrowding the hospital with patients of all ages.

Bretonneau began studying croup in all its stages. Working day and night, he made a detailed analysis of 136 cases. Some recovered, but most of them died. During the course of the

As late as 1878, a diphtheria epidemic killed over 2,000 out of every million in London.

epidemic he performed 60 autopsies on men, women, and children.

In the conclusions presented to the Academy of Medicine in 1826, Bretonneau advanced a novel idea. Diseases are specific, he said. The infectious material which produced a disease always produced that disease only. One of these afflictions produced a false membrane in the throat, extending rapidly down the windpipe and resulting in suffocation. Bretonneau called it diphtherite.

Thus the knowledge of diphtheria was advanced another notch beyond Jurine and Albers. However, no further progress was made for the next half century. Then Edwin Klebs took to microbe hunting.

A brilliant pathologist, Klebs recognized the important role that bacteriology would play in the science of medicine. He applied himself early to a systematic study of the research methods of the young science. In observing cases of typhoid fever, he came across the typhoid bacillus. While examining the lesions of syphilis, he saw corkscrew organisms which he believed were the cause of the disease. Fearing that his methods were imperfect and that his conclusions would be subject to ridicule, he hesitated to announce his observations.

In 1883, a break came at last for Edwin Klebs. Studying the membrane material from the throat of a diphtheria patient, he saw the rodlike, club-shaped microbe that he had seen in previous cases of diphtheria. This time he felt certain of his position, so he published his results.

Diphtheria was one of the first microbial diseases against which a protective vaccine was successfully developed. Its development was the work of two scientists, Frederick Loeffler and Emil Behring.

Loeffler had isolated the diphtheria bacillus discovered by Klebs (now known as the Klebs-Loeffler or K-L bacillus). He demonstrated that there are two kinds of diphtheria bacilli, both morphologically alike. One was harmless, while the other was a ruthless murderer. During his further experiments with diphtheria and guinea pigs, he came upon a puzzle. Many of his little animals became paralyzed and died of diphtheria, yet they showed only slight traces of the disease in their throats.

Loeffler could not fathom this. Was it possible that the animals were dying of a poison manufactured by the germs instead of by the germs themselves? There was a way to find out. Loeffler began growing diphtheria bacilli in bouillon. Filtering the bouillon free of the organisms, he injected the germ-free broth into fresh guinea pigs. It promptly killed them. *Diphtheria poison or "toxin" had been discovered!*

And so, one after another, the scientists added links in the chain of medical progress.

Loeffler then injected guinea pigs with small doses of diphtheria bacilli. It made the animals ill, but they recovered. A month later they were injected with more bacilli. They became only mildly ill. After this, though he repeatedly injected them with heavy doses of the germs—which should have been fatal—the animals showed no ill effects.

What had happened was obvious. Recovery from the first and second inoculations had conferred immunity upon the animals against future attacks of diphtheria. This was a great triumph in itself. But how could this knowledge be made workable for human beings? Who would attempt to inject living men with virulent diphtheria bacilli on the probability that they would become immune?

Dr. Emil Behring gave the answer. Behring was a physician in the German Army after the Franco-Prussian War. The standard dressing for wounds in those days was iodoform. If you visited a hospital dressing station, you would never forget the odor of this compound. Dressing the wounds of soldiers, Behring loathed this odor. But he was curious about its curative effects. What was it in this evil-smelling powder that caused the healing of wounds?

The answer soon came to him. The iodoform itself did not heal the wounds—it was the iodine that did it. During multiplication, the germs produced a chemical product. When this product came in contact with iodoform, a chemical action resulted. Iodine was liberated, and its antiseptic properties killed the organisms. Thus Behring was introduced to a subject which was to play a great part in his later researches. He went to the Hygienic Institute in Berlin, where he found Loeffler working with diphtheria and guinea pigs.

Behring watched Loeffler's experiments with interest. Animals were being injected with diphtheria bacilli. The first shot made them sick, the second induced only a mild illness, and succeeding injections produced no ill effects at all.

Behring's interest turned to excitement. Somewhere, he felt, perhaps only a step beyond Loeffler's guinea pigs, might lie the secret of protecting man against diphtheria. Then an idea came to him. Why not take blood serum from an immunized guinea pig, mix it with diphtheria toxin, inject the mixture (toxin-antitoxin) into a fresh animal, and see what happened? He injected the toxin-antitoxin into the animal, and not the slightest trace of illness developed. The serum of the immunized guinea pig had neutralized the toxin and rendered it inocuous. *Thus was born the practice of antitoxin injections against diphtheria.*

The first injection of diphtheria antitoxin was given to a child in Berlin on Christmas Day, 1891. Since then this form of passive immunity has been widely practiced, with excellent results. So Napoleon's great prize contest was not run in vain. As a result of it, countless millions of children have been saved from a cruel and terrible death.

9

He Brought Back
the Quinine

The men lay on the beach, burning with thirst. Every few minutes one would lift himself to his knees and crawl forward a few inches. Then he would sink slowly to the ground, broken by the fever and the pitiless heat of Bataan.

On a hospital bed a soldier thrust out a feeble hand at the nurse. "My quinine, please," he pleaded.

"Sorry, we have none left," the nurse replied.

Lieutenant Colonel Arthur F. Fischer, of Military Intelligence, one of the unsung heroes of World War II, lay back on his pillow.

As were 85 per cent of the men on Bataan, Colonel Fischer was shaking with malaria. The irony of their situation hit him hard. He had spent 20 years of his life fighting to convince American authorities to grow cinchona trees in the Philippines. Now he and his men were dying as proof that he was right. But he would not die, he told himself—he would not die. For five days he fought the fever, and on the sixth day he sent a note to General Wainwright, asking permission to fly to

Lt. Col. Arthur F. Fischer risked his life to bring cinchona seeds to the United States after the Japanese cut off supplies from the Dutch East Indies.

Mindanao. He would bring back some of the precious bark from the trees that he once planted there.

As he lay in bed, burning with fever, he bitterly recalled the words of Surgeon General Thomas Parran two years before. "Without quinine," Dr. Parran had declared, "no important military operation is possible in the tropics."

For the tortured, fever-ridden American Army on Bataan, this prophesy was now being tragically fulfilled.

It was March 1942, and the Japanese Army was flushed with arrogance by its conquest of Melonesia and all its quinine. Worse yet, their fighter planes commanded the skies of Asia. Colonel Fischer was willing to pay any price to get his hands on the precious quinine bark. For he knew the score.

Seven years before the Japanese invaded Bataan, Colonel Fischer had been head of the Philippine Bureau of Forestry. He had experimentally planted a number of young cinchona trees, the only known source of quinine, on Mindanao. With prophetic insight, he had urged the Government to cultivate this plant instead of relying on the Dutch Quinine Syndicate.

Now he thought despairingly of those trees. Could General Wainwright get him there? Would he be able to harvest some of the cinchona bark and fly it back to Bataan? With quivering hands, he scribbled the note to the General, pleading for help. Feeble as he was, he felt that he could gather some of the bark, have it ground into pulp and flown back to Bataan where it was so desperately needed.

The note was sent to General Wainwright, and shortly afterward the General came to see him. "How much of the bark can you get?" Wainwright asked. "I do not know exactly how much," he replied, "but I know I can get some."

With his defense forces stricken, and the Japanese pressing steadily upon them, General Wainwright set about to get the quinine. But how could he get Colonel Fischer to Mindanao? The sky was dominated by fast Jap planes. The best that General Wainwright could do was to give top priority to Colonel Fischer's mission. With the prayers of his men behind him, Colonel Fischer flew to Mindanao. He made the trip in an old Bellanca commercial plane, condemned three years previously. But now it was a priceless craft.

In plotting the conquest of Melonesia, the Japanese knew what they wanted. For 30 years they had planned, and for 30 years they had worked toward the fulfillment of those plans. When war broke out, they were in a position to seize the tin mines of northern Malay. They grabbed some 5,000 trucks and thousands of acres of rubber trees, and snapped up our jute and hemp supply.

Precious as they were to us, these commodities could be replaced. But Japan's greatest haul could not be replaced. It consisted of several thousand acres of cinchona trees on the uplands of Java, owned by the Dutch. For almost 200 years these trees had given their Dutch owners virtual monopoly of quinine, the only effective weapon against malaria.

In World War I, malaria had played a minor role, for our troops did not have to fight in the tropics. We fought malaria at home by controlling mosquitoes. Only about 7 of every 10,-000 soldiers were hit by it. In World War II, however, our men had to fight in mosquito-infested India, China, the Philippines, and the South Seas. Adequate control was therefore imperative.

Our government had kept a stock of quinine on hand. We had hoarded a 2-year supply of this valuable commodity against an eventual emergency. But this supply was adequate only for peacetime consumption. It could not in any way meet the demands of the armed forces. More and more quinine was needed, and needed urgently. Since there was no way to obtain it, a drug substitute had to be found.

The Germans themselves provided this second line of defense against malaria. Knowing that some day they would be unable to secure enough quinine on the open market, in 1925 they had started an intensive search for a substitute.

The best German doctors were sent to Mediterranean lowlands where malaria was endemic. After testing hundreds of products, they came up in 1935 with a complicated chemical which they called *Atabrine*. The initial results with Atabrine were extremely gratifying. The drug worked faster than quinine and seemed to be equally potent against malaria. Besides, it was easy to take. Three tablets every day for five days would relieve almost any case of malaria. Moreover, it would save valuable space in ships, so essential in wartime.

While seven tons of quinine would help only 25,000 patients, one ton of Atabrine would help 500,000. Its only liability was that it sometimes turned the skin yellow. So what? Nazi military leaders clicked their heels and raised their hands in salute to German genius. A big step forward had been taken toward world conquest, they thought. Little did they know what the morrow would bring.

Wondrous, indeed, are some of the accidents of life. The Germans made the colossal mistake of letting the United States in on the great secret. When they discovered the extent of their mistake, it was already too late to correct it. The great German dye-trust in prewar years had sold the formula of this new drug to the United States. Since they deliberately left out vital elements in the synthesis formula, it is safe to say that little benevolence accompanied this act.

But the Germans had underestimated the ingenuity of American chemists—in this particular case, the wizardry of Dr. A. E. Sherndal, of the Winthrop Chemical Company. This unsung plague fighter immediately went to work on the new drug and put the jigsaw together. By supplying the missing elements, he solved the intricate formula before the guns started booming over the English channel. Subjected to rigid tests by American scientists, Atabrine emerged with flying colors.

Soon after the fateful day December 7, 1941, facilities for the production of Atabrine in large quantities were completed. Winthrop and Merck, two of our largest chemical manufacturers, joined in the mass production of the drug. Atabrine pills were shortly being produced at the rate of 500,000,000 a year. One single Army order in 1943 called for 250,000,000 pills, to be flown to the Pacific, to Africa, to the rubber plantations of Brazil, and elsewhere. Yet we still couldn't get enough of it—

and that is why Colonel Fischer was flying to Mindanao while
his men lay dying on Bataan.

Over Mindanao he surveyed the ground for his trees. He had
had a strange adventure with them. As head of the Philippine
Bureau of Forestry, he had discovered a planter wasting away
from malaria, without a gram of quinine to palliate his fever.
It had made him sick at heart. With all the quinine being
produced in Melonesia, there were those who could not get a
grain of it to relieve their misery!

The Netherlands government in 1921 held a monopoly on
cinchona, sometimes destroying surplus supplies to keep prices
up. Colonel Fischer decided to do something about this cruel
and unjust monopoly. He knew, as did the crafty Dutch Quinine Syndicate, that the only way to acquire cinchona trees was
to secure the seeds. He would smuggle the seeds out and grow
them in an area with the same soil and climate as Java.

The Dutch were not to be caught napping. They guarded
every avenue through which smuggling could be done. There
would be no competition in this field if they could help it.

Colonel Fischer found no opportunity in 1921, but he never
gave up. A year later his chance came. A native farmer, in urgent need of money, came to him for help. Colonel Fischer
made a deal with him. If the farmer would smuggle some cinchona seeds out of Java, the money would be his. Though he
was not keen on running such a risk, the farmer needed the
money desperately and said he would try. He did try—and succeeded.

For 4,000 pesos, he secured a packet of seeds of the very
best cinchona variety. He placed the packet in a sealed tin con-
tainer and gave it to a British sea captain who smuggled it
aboard his ship and carried it to the Philippines.

The seeds did not meet with the ready success that Fischer
had anticipated. Most of them failed to germinate. There was
a drought, and many of those which had germinated into young
seedlings died. To keep the young plants alive, water had to be
carried in pails from a considerable distance by the natives.
Then insects claimed their share. Filled with despair, Colonel

Fischer appealed to the Philippine Malarial Control Board for help to finance the project. The Board refused his request. They had no funds for such a purpose, they said, and anyway, it was not actually a malaria control project!

Colonel Fischer persisted, however, and five years later, in 1927, was at last rewarded. When the first barks were harvested, they contained as much quinine as the trees of Java. The Philippine government was again requested to help, and this time it did. A small plant was built in Manila for the extraction of totaquine, a crude form of quinine. It was not as refined as the finished commercial product but was quite as effective against malaria.

Yet even this small enterprise had fallen into the hands of the Japanese. And so, Colonel Fischer was after it again.

By skillful flying and ducking Japanese fighter planes, Colonel Fischer arrived safely on Mindanao. But he was an exhausted man, little more than a hobbling frame, reeking with malaria. In addition to fever, he had contracted blood poisoning in his arm. Of his usual weight of 150 pounds, he had lost 54; he now weighed only 96 pounds. But they were fighting pounds, alive with purpose. The tragic plight of his men on Bataan spurred him on and seemed to give him strength and courage.

Within two days after his arrival on Mindanao, his faithful assistant, Santos, a Chinese-Filipino, was bringing in the bark. Though handicapped and without machinery or equipment, they found a nearby farmer with a corn grinder which they used to grind the bark to a pulp. For shipping containers they rounded up some abandoned gasoline drums.

Then, after all this, came the terrible message. *Bataan was about to fall.* Word was received from General Wainwright that there was no boat service to Bataan. The quinine could not be shipped. It was now needed more desperately than ever, so some other way of extracting it from the bark and smuggling it out had to be devised.

This was on Easter Sunday, April 5, 1942.

Without the necessary lime, ether, and sulfuric acid to effect the extraction, Fischer found himself up against a stone wall. It was tough enough for a man in sound health, but a thousand times worse for one shaking with malaria. However, with a desperation of impending death, he carried on. A schoolteacher he knew had a small laboratory in his school, and with the help of a priest who had a knowledge of chemistry they were able to get started. They obtained the ether and the sulfuric acid from a hospital; they found the lime in an abandoned soap factory. For mixing vats they used two old bathtubs. Two faithful natives kept bringing in the bark, and within three days the little group began the tedious work of extraction.

Then suddenly everything was knocked over. Only five days after he arrived at Mindanao, Colonel Fischer heard the tragic news that Bataan had fallen. The Japanese were already in possession of the island. All was lost. All their efforts had amounted to nought; in a few days the Japs would be overrunning Mindanao.

The long years of labor with his cinchona trees facing calamity, and all his dreams shattered, nevertheless Colonel Fischer stayed on to rescue some of the seeds. So vital was this last-straw attempt to save the cinchona seeds considered by the Army, that a plane was sent to Mindanao to rush Colonel Fischer to Australia with two tin containers filled with seeds. He departed from Mindanao on one of the last planes to leave the Philippines.

Arriving in Australia, Fischer at once was put aboard one of the fastest ships to San Francisco and from there flown directly to Washington. Across the world he sped with the precious seeds pressed close to him. Only on his arrival at the Capital did he surrender them. They were taken immediately to Glenn Dale, Maryland, and planted under glass by the Department of Agriculture. Young plants from this nursery are now producing quinine on the United States plantation in Costa Rica, a living and inspiring monument to the intrepid heroism of Colonel Arthur Fischer.

Today new drugs and new methods of control are being developed in our unceasing war on malaria. But to Colonel Fischer and the others who defied death to bring back the quinine, we owe a special debt of gratitude. Their glowing record of human courage surely will not be forgotten.

~~~ **10** ~~~

Search for the Miracle Tree

The fascinating story of quinine did not begin with Colonel Fischer on the island of Mindanao. The magic of cinchona bark had been known many years previously. Though physicians had not the vaguest idea of the nature of malaria, the Indians of Peru and probably of Bolivia and Colombia had been using quinine for years. It was from the Peruvian Indians that Europeans learned of this magic tree whose bark, when brewed as a tea, could reduce malaria fever.

Numerous attempts have been made to credit early Jesuits with the discovery of quinine, but historical evidence has not corroborated this claim. Certain Peruvian tribes, it is believed, possessed a knowledge of the curative powers of cinchona bark, but they kept it from the white invaders, hoping, perhaps, that eventually malaria would drive them out of South America.

When Pizzaro made his conquest of Peru in 1537, many of his followers were stricken and died of malaria. If the early Jesuits had known of this secret, they certainly would have informed Pizzaro, who could have used this bark not only to save his own men but also to exploit it as a source of gold. However, there is no mention of cinchona in the records of Pizzaro or of José de Acosta, who wrote the natural history of

South America. Nor has Gracilasso, who discussed many native remedies, mentioned it. But whoever did make the discovery, it undoubtedly was a pure accident.

The strange story of cinchona bark goes far back in European history. In the early seventeenth century, Portugal, once the leading European aspirant for colonies in the New World, declined rapidly. The Pilgrims had celebrated their seventh Christmas in Massachusetts, and Philip IV of Spain, flushed with power and gold, had built up an impressive empire on the vast continent of South America.

In 1628, King Philip decided to send Don Louis Mendez, the Count of Cinchona, to rule the young, rich empire. He was to consolidate all its natural resources for the benefit of the Spanish throne. The Count had a beautiful young wife. When they arrived in Lima, capital of Peru, some time in September, they immediately moved into a palatial residence.

One evening, a few months later, they sat down to supper, while their retinue of servants waited upon them.* A mosquito alighted on the beautiful lady's neck. A few days later she was ordered to bed, burning with fever. The doctor came and gave her some medicine, but there was no improvement in her condition. For almost two weeks she lay shaking between life and death. Then one day a young Indian raced into the palace with a letter and a packet of brown bark. He said that he came from the Spanish magistrate of Loxa, who had heard of the Countess' illness. "Brew the bark in wine," were his directions, "and take several times a day." The magistrate wrote that he himself had suffered from malaria and had been cured by an Indian who had given him the brew.

After reading the letter, the Countess promptly gave it to her doctor who was present. Seeing the instructions, he shook his head. The bark was unknown to him. It had not been mentioned in any of the medical journals of Spain nor by any of the old botanists. But since the Countess was dying, anything

---

* Numerous conflicting stories have been told of this little adventure, and their authenticity is still being questioned today. But quinine did come through.

was worth trying. Therefore, he advised her to carry out the magistrate's instructions.

After taking the brew for a number of days, Countess Cinchona recovered. However, her sickness was more than she had anticipated in the New World, so she decided to return to Spain. "Too many miasmas in Lima," she observed, ruefully.

Taking a packet of the bark with her, she left Lima within a few weeks after her recovery. But her destiny had been sealed. On the homeward journey the unfortunate Countess died of another complication, and her remains were buried in Colombia, the nearest Spanish domain. The bark which she had taken with her was sent to Spain, tested on several malarial patients, and proved to be a great success.

As in the Gold Rush of 1848, an electric wave awoke the populace. Discovery of the precious commodity aroused intense interest in South America. Not only did the gold glitter in their eyes, but the quina tree did too. All Europe clamored for the bark. The first shipload to reach the Continent fetched exorbitant prices.

This was the beginning of the battle for the bark among the nations of Europe. It started in Seville, spread throughout Spain, and hit Portugal, France, and England. Under the name of "Peruvian Bark" or "Powder of the Countess," it was gobbled up on the markets. Realizing its potentialities, the Jesuits dispensed it as "Jesuit Powder."

Now the quacks saw their opportunity. Boldest of the medical quacks of his day was Robert Talbor, of Cambridge, England, perpetrator of one of the most widespread and successful hoaxes ever recorded in medical history.

A cocky and restless young man, Talbor had been a medical student at St. John's College in Cambridge. However, he disappeared before his first term was up, a few years later reappearing in London and posing as a full-fledged practitioner. London's staid and conventional doctors made an effort to chase him from the city, but they could not hide one vital fact. He was able to cure malaria fever, and they could not.

The College of Physicians then decided to take a hand in the matter. Whether he could cure malaria or not, they held that Talbor was a quack and should be exposed. But Talbor was not idle. He had gained the confidence and the friendship of many of the King's trusted men. One day he was summoned to the sickbed of Charles II; he cured the King's malaria. Then he cured Lady Mordant of the disease, and forthwith the King knighted him, making the young quack his official physician.

"Scoundrel! Rascal! Impostor!" The dignified College of Physicians resorted to name-calling. The King was being misled by false friends, they hotly declared, and they formed a committee to go and enlighten His Majesty.

But Talbor's friends were also at work. When the committee sought admission to the presence of the King, they were rebuffed. Backed by His Majesty, bounteously hailed as the wonder doctor and "the greatest physician in all of Europe," Talbor now became bold. His remedy, he claimed, was the only cure for malaria. "The Jesuit Powder is worthless," he asserted. "Peruvian Bark is overrated; it does not really cure, and its after-effects are dangerous." His patients beat a trail to his door. For fabulous fees, he cured their malaria and reaped a fortune.

Not satisfied with the fame he had won in London, Talbor decided to invade the Continent. Just as he reached France, the Dauphin of Paris was stricken with malaria. The doctors tried every remedy, except Peruvian Bark, but without success. Talbor promptly cured the Dauphin and became a French hero. He was knighted and honored wherever he went. King Louis was ever so grateful—he offered Talbor a position at Court, extended royal patronage to him, and persuaded him to accept many expensive presents.

The wily, beaver-hatted, dapper-boy from London refused to accept any gifts or compensation. "It is a privilege," he declared, bowing low before the French King, "to serve his Royal Highness, the King of France."

"Then, give me the formula," the King replied, "that France may possess this great secret."

Talbor nearly hit the ceiling. He stood there speechless. How could he refuse the King of France such a royal request?

At length Talbor regained his composure and replied, "I shall gladly reveal the formula to His Majesty, upon this condition alone: that the formula be kept a strict secret until after my death."

Louis accepted the agreement. Talbor returned to England and died about a year later. Upon his death, as a special gift from the King to the French nation, the formula was published in all the French newspapers. Talbor had written down three items:

1. 6 drachms of rose leaves
2. 2 ounces of lemon juice
3. A strong infusion of Peruvian Bark

The first two items did the camouflaging; the Peruvian Bark wrought the cures—much to the embarrassment of physicians.

Peruvian bark had made good. It appeared in 1677, for the first time, in the British pharmacopeia and on all accepted lists of medicine. Botanists changed the name from Peruvian bark to Cinchona, in honor of the Countess of Cinchona, through whose efforts the bark had been introduced into Europe.

The South American sources were now wantonly exploited. Greed led both Spaniards and Indians to plunder the cinchona forests without thought of the future. One European nation after another made fruitless efforts to smuggle out cinchona seeds. Failing in all their attempts, the rival governments offered fabulous rewards and honors to any citizen who could find the chemicals in cinchona bark that cured malaria.

Paris was beautiful in the spring of 1789. Pierre Joseph Pelletier, a young French chemist, and his young friend, Joseph B. Caventou, a pharmacist, met one day in a science laboratory— and proceeded to make scientific history. Why couldn't they embark on a project to extract chemicals from plants? Both were familiar with the researches of Serteurner, who had found morphine in opium. The two young men decided to pattern their researches along similar lines.

When they parted company that afternoon, they were ready to set the world on fire. They began with ipecac, a new drug imported from South America as a cure for dysentery and diarrhea. From this they extracted a chemical which they called *emetine*. Then they worked on a highly poisonous plant called Strychnos and extracted *strychnine*. But these extracts had no practical commercial value.

"What we want to work on next," said the younger scientist, Caventou, "is cinchona bark. Cinchona extract has some relationship to the alkaloids. If we can find the source of the alkaloids, we might find the source of the chemical which cures malaria."

"But why cinchona bark?" Pelletier asked skeptically. "Why not work on some other plant?"

"Because," Caventou replied, "cinchona is the most important drug today. The world is ridden with malaria—millions are dying and millions more are wasting away. The man who can find a cure for malaria will save the lives of millions at a single stroke. The alkaloids seem to offer the best possibilities."

Though Pelletier did not share his partner's optimism in the search for the alkaloids, the basis of the quinine in cinchona bark, nevertheless he decided to try.

"First," he said, "let us examine all the available literature on cinchona bark and see what we can find and which mistakes to avoid. That will save time."

So the search for the alkaloids was on.

The young scientists imported literature from England, Portugal, Sweden, and Germany. They discovered that the Portuguese chemist, Dr. Gomez, had worked for years on cinchona bark, trying to extract the chemical that would cure malaria. He had found several but nothing alkaloid and none that would cure malaria. The prospects were not bright. They admired the technique of Dr. Gomez so much, though, that they decided to adopt it with minor changes.

In a few days they succeeded in extracting from *gray* cinchona bark a quantity of fine crystals. But, alas, they were the same sort of crystals that Gomez had found years before.

Pelletier was discouraged. He was ready to turn to something else. But not Caventou.

"We've only just begun," he pleaded. "Let's not give up now. Let's do some researches on *yellow* cinchona bark."

"Do you think the color of the bark can make a difference?" the other asked. "Cinchona bark is cinchona bark to me. Yellow or gray, it has the same properties."

"Don't be so sure," young Caventou replied. "Dr. Gomez did his experiments with the gray bark. Let's see what happens with the yellow bark."

What actually happened with the yellow bark has become a part of the history of quinine.

The two scientists found in the yellow bark exactly what they were looking for. They found fine crystals, soluble in acid and in alcohol, like the crystals extracted from the gray bark. Unlike the latter, however, these were soluble in ether. The men called the new product *quinine* from the Peruvian word for the Cinchona quina tree. Here at last was a pure chemical that would cure malaria fever.

So a new era began. Next to gold, cinchona bark became the most priceless commodity on earth. Since the South American supply was inadequate, the nation which could discover a natural source of quinine in Europe, or produce it synthetically, would have a monopoly of the world's markets. France had a head start in the discoveries of Pelletier and Caventou, but they had only *extracted* quinine. They did not produce quinine from cinchona bark and, besides, cinchona trees grew only in South America.

Surely there was a way to produce quinine synthetically. The French Society of Pharmacy offered a prize of $10,000 to anyone who succeeded in making synthetic quinine. Everywhere chemists thumbed their way through the literature on quinine, searching for clues.

Many new attempts to smuggle cinchona seeds into Europe met with dismal failure. Peruvians were jealous of their priceless possession and tried to keep it within their borders. Moreover, the long overland journey through the tropical jungles of Peru to the source of the cinchona trees made it tough for anyone to smuggle either the shrubs or the seeds to a port where they could be delivered to a ship.

The first almost successful attempt had been made by a Frenchman nearly a century before. It was a harrowing experience. In 1738, the French Academy of Sciences had sent four scientists to make longitudinal and meridian measurements on the equator to determine the circumference of the earth. One of these, Charles Marie de la Condamine, feeling that he had been mistreated, resigned from the group after reaching Peru. Lacking sufficient funds to return to France, he put his wits to work. If he could only secure cinchona seeds or seedlings for the Academy, his passage on any French ship bound for Europe would be assured. The success of such an attempt, he knew, certainly would exonerate him and justify his desertion, if nothing else would.

Learning several native dialects, de la Condamine started out along the Andes. He traveled for many weeks, befriending Indians along the trail, and at last reached Loxa, in Peru, where the cinchona bark flourished. Through the friendship of a priest he was given the name of a Spaniard living in Loxa.

After visiting the forests and observing how cinchona bark was harvested, de la Condamine decided to smuggle some of the very youngest plants to the coast and ship them aboard the first ship bound for France. With the aid of his Spanish host, he carefully dug up the most promising young seedlings and transplanted them into small boxes of rich soil. When these had taken root, he and his trusted Indian companion set out for the coast.

For days they crossed mountain ranges and penetrated dense jungles. After more than two weeks of extreme hardship, with less than a day's journey from their goal, disaster overtook them. While shooting the rapids of a stream, their skiff was capsized and the two men barely escaped with their lives. Every plant was lost in the heavy current.

The three remaining scientists finished their mission in Ecuador. Two of them departed for France. The third, Joseph de Jussieu, decided to visit other parts of Peru to study the exuberant plant life, planning to return to France the following year.

Fascinated by the abundance of plant life in Peru, de Jussieu remained 30 years. He collected new plants and wrote them up in his journals while traveling through the interior. At last, feeling that his work was completed, he decided to return to France. Like de la Condamine, he too would render a patriotic service to his country.

With no knowledge of the other's attempt to take seedlings to France, he decided against this scheme. The risk was too great, he felt, and the young plants too cumbersome. Instead of seedlings he would take seeds. These he could smuggle out and, with the right environment, they would certainly germinate.

De Jussieu carefully collected thousands of seeds and sealed them in air-tight tin cans. Then he enclosed the cans in a small wooden box which he determined always to keep under his arm. This plan worked well for a time, and he reached Buenos Aires with his treasure intact. But the very care which he had given the little box was its undoing.

A servant he had hired in Buenos Aires noticed how carefully his master guarded the little box, keeping it always within sight. Surely it contained gold, the young Indian surmised. On his last night in Buenos Aires, while getting ready to sail, de Jussieu stepped out of his room for a moment. That was the end. The young Indian and the little box vanished into thin air.

Torn with grief, de Jussieu sailed for France the next day. With the sadness and the heartache of a shattered dream, he went back to his beloved France. But there were men there with great hearts. He was acclaimed a hero. For his detailed reports and descriptions of the unusual plant life in South America, he was honored by the French Academy of Sciences.

But Joseph de Jussieu never knew what was taking place. He had become insane.

And so men lived and died in search for a cure for malaria. Always there was a valiant fighter to lead the way, but always

the odds were too great, always the selfish interests too powerful. And still people suffered and died in agony, and their
memory was washed away in the oceans of tears that poured
down the river of time.

Thus life moved on, and the search for quinine moved on
with it. In 1852 a young Englishman named Charles Ledger
came upon the scene. He had spent some time near Lake Titi-
caca in Peru, so he too joined the mad scramble for the miracle
tree. Ledger had an advantage over the others. Having traded
on a small scale in cinchona bark, he could obtain reliable information about the best species.

To make a collection of the best seeds, Ledger sent a trusted
Indian servant to cross the Bolivian border. The Indian was
caught by the ever-watchful Bolivians and jailed. Two years
later he turned up in Peru with 14 pounds of seeds. Ledger
sent these seeds to his brother George in England.

Here at last is where the tide turned.

George offered to sell the seeds to the British government,
but the Crown was not interested. Then he offered them to the
Dutch. Just as an experiment, the Dutch government bought
one pound of Ledger's seeds for 1,000 francs and planted them
in Java. Just one pound! But this was the little plant that moved
mountains, sent armies on the march, sent war planes scream-
ing over Java, and sent the feeble Colonel Fischer on his solo
expedition of mercy.

Within two decades after planting the Ledger seeds, the
Dutch virtually controlled the quinine trade. The seeds turned
out to be the best producers, with a quinine content equal to
the finest in South America. So profitable was their cultivation
that it brought an end to the South American trade.

The Dutch were now masters of the miracle tree, a position
they maintained until World War II, when the Japanese took
Melonesia, cutting off all supplies. And that is how Colonel
Arthur F. Fischer came to do his bit for humanity on that hot,
sunny morning of 1942 in his precious, though battered, Bellanca plane.

∞ 11 ∞

A Vicious Female

Men fought malaria, but they didn't fight its cause. Like Quixote, they fought windmills. Deadly, elusive, it mystified men for a thousand years. Now we shall see what we were really fighting.

The decline of Rome has been closely linked with the Anopheles mosquito. During the days of Caesar's civil wars, over 60 per cent of the Roman population was infected, and thousands of his soldiers were incapacitated. Caesar himself was a victim of the "Roman airs," as malaria was known in Rome. Pliny, who was killed in the Vesuvius eruption A.D. 79, suffered from malaria.

The word "malaria" is itself of Roman origin. Tori, in 1700, named it "mal-aria" in the belief that the fever was caused by bad airs or miasmas. Forty years later, in 1740, while Horace Walpole was visiting Italy, he united both words into one—"malaria."

The effect of the Anopheles upon the early Romans can be seen by their abandonment of the beautiful city of Ninfa. Not far from Rome, it was in its heyday the favorite residence of Pope Alexander III. Ninfa was also cherished by the early Christians because it was visited by the apostle Paul while on

82

his way to Rome. But the city was so malarious it had to be abandoned. Today all that remains of its glorious past are its old foundations and the dust of years gone by.

The capture and the invasion of Rome by the Goths spear-headed the disease through most of Europe. Refugees from Rome carried it into France, England, Germany, and other countries. By the time of the Crusades, toward the close of the eleventh century, malaria had gradually conquered most of the continent.

The origin of malaria in America is obscure. Soon after the arrival of the colonists, it began to flourish in the Virginia marshes. It spread unhampered until the arrival in 1680 of the buccaneer doctor, Lionel Wafer, who brought almost half a ton of cinchona bark from Peru.

When the American Revolution began, malaria became a serious problem in the colonies. From his headquarters in New Jersey, Washington was plagued by the disease.

Probably the worst enemy American soldiers had to face in World War II was the female Anopheles mosquito. On the Pacific Islands they had to build greater defenses against the insect than against their human foe. Plunging into impenetrable jungle, into swamplands infested with Anophelines, our men suffered torture and slow death. In this respect they were no match for the Japanese who, long prepared for such an eventuality, carried ample supplies of quinine tablets.

In Sicily, more casualties were caused by malaria during World War II than from the military operations of the enemy. During the construction of the Burma Road, more than 50 per cent of the laborers in certain areas died as a result of the disease.

Unlike diphtheria, typhus, cholera, typhoid, and several others, malaria has defied all vaccines. Nor is there any sure cure for the disease, in spite of the great efforts of scientists

to find one. The only protection against it is avoidance of the
mosquito which carries the parasites in her salivary glands.

Although malaria has been the world's number one disease
for countless centuries, only toward the close of the nineteenth
century has any definite knowledge been gained of its cause.
Except that it was in some way associated with swamplands,
little was known of it. It remained for Charles Louis Alphonse
Laveran, the French physician, to begin to unravel the mystery.

Dr. Laveran was a medical officer stationed at Constantine,
Algeria, where malaria was rife. With an army of subjects
available, he began a systematic examination of the blood of
malaria victims. While thus engaged, on November 6, 1880,
in a blood smear he saw waving, hairlike projections which
proved to be protozoan, the microbe now known as *Plasmo-
dium vivax*.

Important though this discovery was, it did not solve the
entire problem. How did the microbe get into the blood stream
of its victim? And where did it come from? To these questions
there was no immediate answer.

Some blood-sucking insect, probably the mosquito, might
be responsible, Dr. Laveran felt. This was only a guess, however, and proof was lacking. Many people doubted Laveran's
demonstrations and insisted that the objects he had seen were
in no way connected with the disease. They still claimed that
foul air arising from swamps and decayed vegetable matter, or
"the disturbance of the soil that has long lain fallow," was
responsible for the disease.

Seventeen years later, in 1897, Ronald Ross and Giovanni
Battista Grassi proved that Laveran was correct. But they also
went a long step further. They discovered the insect involved
in the transmission of malaria and traced the complete life
cycle of the parasite.

Dr. Ross was an officer in the British Indian Medical Service.
He had heard of Laveran's discovery of the malarial parasites
in human blood and the suspicion placed on the mosquito as
their carrier. But Ross was skeptical. In his belief that Laveran

was wrong, he tried to prove it by capturing mosquitoes and examining them. Finding none of the parasites that the doctor in Algeria had described, Ross concluded that Laveran was in error—that malaria was not a germ disease at all.

Then Ross went to Europe on a furlough. While in London he met Patrick Manson, a successful English physician. Manson had already shown the part played by the mosquito in the transmission of another disease, filariasis, and was greatly interested in the malarial problem. He succeeded in convincing Ross that Laveran was probably correct in his suspicion of the mosquito. Then he showed Ross some of the malarial parasites and suggested ways of improving his research methods.

Ross returned to India with a consuming passion to verify the cause of malaria and discover its means of transmission. He began caging mosquitoes at random, feeding them on malarial Hindus, and then examining the insects. But he saw nothing resembling the parasites which Manson had shown him in London. Obviously, something was still wrong: it was his technique, or the mosquitoes he examined, or, not unlikely, Laveran's idea.

Later events proved that the error was not with the theory but with himself. Ross had been examining the insects too soon after they had obtained their blood meal, without allowing sufficient time for the growth of the parasites in the insects' bodies.

On August 19, 1894, he killed two mosquitoes which had been fed four days previously on the blood of malarial patients. To his great delight he found the organisms in the stomachs of the pests. Repeated examination convinced him at last that Laveran's theory was true. By infecting birds with the germs, Ross was able to trace the cycle of the malarial parasites.

However, a third and final problem still remained unsolved. Laveran had demonstrated the cause of the disease, and Ross had spotted the carrier. But there were many species of mosquitoes. To which species did this insect belong? Were all mosquitoes carriers of malarial parasites?

This phase of the investigation was soon assumed by the

Italian zoologist, G. B. Grassi, and his associates. After some intensive field work they not only identified the exact species of mosquitoes but also demonstrated the complete life cycle of the malarial parasite in human beings.

To test the validity of his discovery, Grassi performed tests on humans. By these tests he proved, in the fall of 1898, that malarial parasites were transmitted by the bite of the mosquito we now know as the Anopheles.

Only the female Anopheles carries malaria germs. The female requires animal blood every three or four days for the nutrition of her egg-forming tissues. To obtain this blood she will fly as far as two miles if she cannot find an animal closer. Unlike other insects, she does not return to a "home" but continues to roam over a fairly large area. Therefore, a single female mosquito can infect a number of people. She remains quiet in dark corners during the day, but at night she begins to fly about.

When this mosquito is ready to lay her eggs, she goes in search of water and deposits them on its surface. Within three or four days the eggs hatch into "wigglers" or larvae, which feed on tiny green water plants. These larvae develop rapidly. Ten days after the eggs are laid, they undergo a metamorphosis into fat pupae. Two or three days later, the back of the larva splits open, and the young mosquito struggles out.

Female mosquitoes are well adapted to jabbing animal tissues. When they puncture the skin of a malaria victim, a small amount of their saliva flows into the puncture. This substance contains a poison—which causes the itching—and prevents coagulation of the blood. The victim's blood, already swarming with malarial parasites, is then sucked up into the alimentary canal of the insect.

Soon growth begins. If the mosquito bites a second victim, she injects into him some of the parasites from her salivary glands. These organisms are so small that they easily work their way into the blood stream and attack the red blood cells. They begin to multiply rapidly, one microbe dividing into several. It is the breaking up of the cells and the release of the parasites into the blood stream that causes the fever and the chills.

The search for a cure for malaria was intensified during World War II, and a long list of new drug compounds resulted. Except for toxic variations, they produce about the same results as quinine. The famous SN 7618, heralded as a medical miracle and supposedly capable of stopping the disease in its tracks, has proved to be effective against only one species of malaria. During the war the Government spent more than $7 million seeking a cure.

Malaria is tragic not only because it kills, but also because it is the world's greatest single cause of invalidism. It is insidious rather than dramatic in its effect, and it results in an increased number of deaths from other causes. It stunts physical and mental growth, blights agriculture, and stifles commerce and industry. Stricken countries cannot achieve normal economic and social progress. Notable among these, of course, is India, with its teeming millions, many of whom are only half-alive.

When the World Health Organization was set up in 1948, malaria was given top priority. The WHO aim was "to eliminate malaria from the world as a major public health problem." From the outset, WHO placed its faith mainly in campaigns of house-spraying with DDT. Demonstration teams were sent to any country requesting them. As a result, many countries succeeded not only in reducing malaria but also in suppressing almost all traces of the disease. It looked as though the end was near.

But then the mosquito struck back. It was receding over vast areas when the first warning reached WHO that all was not well. In 1951, one type of malaria mosquito began to resist DDT; then another; then still another. Resistance had set in almost everywhere.

Most of the countries concerned had planned on maintaining control indefinitely with DDT-spraying. But now it was obvious that another approach was needed. In 1955, enough evidence had been accumulated to point to a new policy: *total eradication*—that is, definite elimination of the disease by an intensive campaign limited in time.

The World Health Assembly, meeting in Mexico in 1955, made a firm decision. Malaria must be eradicated before mosquitoes had time to develop resistance to the various insecticides in use. Therefore, it set up a World Malaria Fund to help finance this all-out campaign.

Malaria eradication is possible, the Assembly declared, because the blood parasite of malaria in man is no longer active after three years. If the cycle of transmission (man-to-mosquito-to-man) can be broken, and no new cases occur during those three years, then the spraying campaign can stop. Mosquitoes will still be present, but there will be few sick people from whom they can become infected and pass on the infection.

In 1959 the World Health Organization began its greatest battle to control malaria on a global scale. For the next five years, WHO announced a need for $32 million to give necessary help to countries undertaking malaria eradication. But the work is going ahead at last. And that's what matters most.

While malaria struck 300 million people yearly in 1950 and caused 3 million deaths a year, these figures have now been cut in half!

Infant mortality, too, is decreasing everywhere. Surely the total results of malaria control to humanity will be dramatic and far-reaching. It is an exciting prospect for all the world.

∿∿ 12 ∿∿

Tropic Graveyard

"They lived and died many centuries ago. Little else is known about them."

So wrote a famous explorer of the Mayas of Central America less than 50 years ago. And indeed, that's all anyone knew about this ancient people at the close of the nineteenth century. Today, however, we know much more. Archeological discoveries among the jungle ruins of their abandoned cities tell us the tragic story. It is the story of a people who, without benefit of contemporary influences, were able to develop a noble civilization. However, at the height of their hard-won prosperity, they became the victims of that terror of the tropics—yellow fever.

Today all that is left of their once-flourishing culture—a grim reminder of the ruthlessness of the microbe—are foundations of their buried cities in Central America, reclaimed long ago despite the unrelenting growth of the jungle.

The Aztecs seem to have been wiser builders than the Mayas. They constructed their cities on elevated ground, far away from swamps and marshes. The Aztec civilization survived in splendor for many centuries until it was crushed in the early sixteenth century by the Spaniards.

89

Panama was the most colossal graveyard of yellow fever victims in the world, until Dr. Walter Reed and his colleagues identified the *Stegomyia* mosquito as the carrier.

In spite of their architectural skill, their unsurpassed pottery-making, and magnificent pyramids and temples, the Mayas built unwisely. They built in the lowlands not far enough from many bodies of water and too close to the sea. Thus, yellow fever was able to move in upon them. In a few centuries it decimated their population and undermined their civilization.

Starting A.D. 300,* the Mayas were visited by a yearly pestilence of yellow fever which their hieroglyphics record as "black vomit." In 1454, less than 50 years before the voyages of Columbus, they suffered the severest epidemic in their history. Historians believe that this disaster brought about their dispersion as a race.

The strangling arms of yellow fever reached far. At the time of the Spanish conquest, they had already stretched forth from Central America to Mexico. The disease was probably introduced into that country by infected Aztec warriors and traders returning from the land of the Mayas. Cortez, during his invasion of Mexico in 1519, found many natives suffering from the fever. Several of his own followers contracted it and died.

Nor did the adventurous dons escape this silent enemy. In 1493 they encountered it in Santo Domingo and three years later in Santa Cruz. When Columbus arrived at Isabela, according to Oviedo y Valdés, he found the native Arawaks suffering from a yellow fever epidemic. Soon his explorers were attacked by it, "so that they became jaundiced and so yellow they looked as if they had been tinted with saffron and so sick that they soon died."

That is how the name "yellow fever" came into existence.

Several historians have discounted the stories that yellow fever existed in Santo Domingo in 1493. To them it seems more probable that the disease was brought to the West Indies directly from Africa at a much later date.

The introduction of yellow fever into the Caribbean islands, these dissenters claim, was coincidental with the early slave

* The Mayan civilization is supposed to have reached its height A.D. 200 to 1450.

traffic. After the Spaniards had established settlements on the islands, their ruthless brutality soon exterminated the natives. Those not killed by the severity of the tasks imposed upon them were driven to suicide. Without free labor to work their mines and plantations, the Spaniards began to import the more hardy African Negroes. Coming from the West Coast, where yellow fever was rampant, they apparently brought the disease to the islands with them.

There is good reason to believe that yellow fever invaded the West Indies from Central America too. In the American colonies the disease established an easy foothold, probably gaining entrance through Colonial-West Indian trade. At any rate, yellow fever took a firm hold in America, and, before the close of the eighteenth century, had become a serious problem. Between 1700 and 1800 no fewer than 32 epidemics of this pestilence bore down on America. It remained endemic in many sections until the beginning of the present century, when the cause of yellow fever was discovered and control measures introduced.

The New England settlers were also assailed by the disease. Encircled by hostile Indians, menaced by hunger and the pestilence, these early settlers were indeed a harassed group. The first major yellow fever outbreak occurred in Salem, Massachusetts, in 1692. A few years later Philadelphia had its first visitation. For almost a century the New England states had a respite, but the New Haven epidemic of 1794 and the one in New York in 1795, which killed 800 persons, served as a reminder that no one was invulnerable.

The Philadelphia yellow fever epidemic of 1793 was almost as disastrous as London's "Black Death" of 1348. The City of Brotherly Love had had outbreaks of the pestilence before, but they were mere trifles compared with the visitation of 1793. Wiping out more than a tenth of the population of Philadelphia, it was, outside of the influenza epidemic of 1918, the most severe in America.

Panic seized everyone. Adding to the hysteria was the tolling of the bells. This had been ordered by the city officials to proclaim the presence of the plague. However, instead of sobering the populace, it produced pandemonium. People fled in every direction, deserting homes and friends, forsaking husbands and wives. Their only thought was escape.

The epidemic not only aroused wide concern for Philadelphians, it also revealed the confusion which prevailed in the highest medical circles concerning yellow fever. What caused the epidemic? Was it imported from a foreign country? Did it start as an epidemic or was its epidemic nature spread by contagion? These were burning questions which the epidemiologists had to face.

Help came from an unexpected source. It is to the eternal credit of our early leaders that they so often stepped out of their chosen calling to pitch in where they were needed most. Two great figures in the United States at the time were Dr. Benjamin Rush and Noah Webster. With characteristic zeal, both undertook to find the cause of the epidemic. That they did not find it was not due to lack of effort.

Dr. Rush, the greatest medical name connected with Colonial America, was a Quaker. One of the signers of the Declaration of Independence, he contributed enormously to American public life. He was a ground-breaker for American psychiatry—perhaps the first American physician to show a genuine interest in the condition of the insane. To him, the insane were sick people rather than criminals, and were entitled to the most humanitarian treatment. Giving more concrete form to his beliefs, he suggested occupational therapy, better food and housing, and more advanced psychiatric methods. He advocated reforms in penal institutions and was one of the foremost fighters for the abolition of slavery.

At the time of the yellow fever epidemic, Dr. Rush was practicing medicine in Philadelphia. Working tirelessly during the emergency, he visited hundreds of patients when other doctors had fled the city. He did not quit until he, too, was stricken.

Eager to get to the root of the disease, Dr. Rush followed many trails. After completing his survey, he declared, "The source of the yellow fever epidemic is to be found right here in Philadelphia." A load of coffee on the wharf near Arch Street had become putrefied. The odor resulting from this decomposition, he believed, was the immediate cause of the outbreak. The coffee was removed, yet the pestilence remained. But Rush did not give up. He had an explanation. Admitting his previous error, he now laid the blame squarely on man. Man had infringed upon nature, he declared. He had built mill-ponds near the city, and the noxious odors from putrid vegetation had polluted the air. This pollution causes the disease, he concluded.

Almost parallel with the best medical opinion of 1800 respecting the origin of yellow fever was the pronouncement of another prominent figure, Noah Webster. Webster is chiefly known as a linguist and lexicographer. He was an essayist, author of the phenomenal best seller, *The American Spelling Book*, and the *American Dictionary of the English Language*. In scientific circles, however, he was an outstanding epidemiological investigator.

Shocked by the devastating epidemic, Webster laid aside his dictionary and pitched in. He began to gather data by a highly original method. He sent out questionnaires to physicians in New Haven, Boston, Baltimore, Philadelphia, and New York, requesting them to set down their observations on yellow fever. No doubt this was the origin of the ubiquitous poll, of which there are so many.

Two opposing schools regarding the yellow fever epidemic sprang up. One claimed that the disease was of foreign origin. Its occurrence in America, this group felt, invariably was associated with the arrival of ships from foreign ports. Examples of this were the outbreak of yellow fever in New York and New Haven in 1794 and 1795 when ships from Martinique and Port-au-Prince had arrived in New York. The disease was of a contagious nature, they maintained, and was spread from person to person by contact or by coming within "ten paces" of the contaminated.

The other group did not attempt to attribute the outbreak to any direct cause. Yellow fever originated locally, they agreed, and was not contagious but rather was caught from the air. Webster sided with the noncontagious group, declaring, "The outbreak was due to corruption of the atmosphere, the pestilential nature of the air. It was a heightened form of unusual summer fever."

Emulating the Greeks, who kindled roaring fires in Athens during the great plague, Philadelphians lighted bonfires to purify the air. To ward off the demon, they fired muskets and ignited gunpowder during the night. Thus did they battle the microbe in 1793.

In that year the Philadelphia catastrophe was curiously matched by an outbreak of yellow fever on the French island of Saint Lucia. Today, some distance up beautiful Morne Fortune, lies a cemetery hidden by strangling growths of tropical foliage. The grave mounds are no longer distinguishable from the natural sloping of the hill. Those once enclosed by stone masonry have lost their protection. Tree roots have split the rocks asunder, scattering their fragments helter-skelter down the rugged slopes. But whatever time has done to this strange burial place, it can never efface the indelible memories left behind by yellow fever.

The year 1793 marked the beginning of a decisive French-English struggle for Saint Lucia, key to many Caribbean islands. In April, a British force of 12,000 men, clicking heels to the command of Sir Ralph Abercromby, landed at Anse de Choc. Weak with fever, the French garrison offered little resistance. The British stalwarts captured Morne Fortune and with it went the whole island.

What sharp patterns are etched in the rock of time by the microbe! While he sailed away to seize Guadaloupe, Abercromby left Sir John Moore with 5,000 troops to garrison the island. This was in June. By the end of September, 3,500 of Moore's men had fallen, not to enemy action, but to yellow fever. Five hundred others became ill, which left only 1,000 fit for duty. Death claimed two officers and seventeen more men on the very day the regiment embarked for another island, leaving their comrades on Morne Fortune.

The French had far more than they bargained for in the tropics. Some 70 years before their Panama Canal adventure, yellow fever had defeated a French army on the island of Haiti. For more than a century France had landlorded it over this Caribbean island. Her rule had become so unpopular with the natives that in 1791 they rebelled and took up arms against their former masters.

Napoleon, deciding that it was about time to crush the rebellion, in 1801 dispatched an army of 25,000 soldiers under the command of General Charles Victor Emmanuel Leclerc to subdue the rebels. The French Army landed at Cap Français and soon defeated (1802) the poorly equipped Negroes. Toussaint L'Ouverture, their leader, went into hiding. Without him, his broken army was lost. But not for long. Soon Jean Jacques Dessalines, another leader, rallied them into a fighting force of 25,000 men. By guerilla tactics, he continued resistance against the French army.

Then, as time went on, yellow fever came to their aid. An epidemic broke out among the French troops and wrought havoc. Scores died daily, and hundreds lay helpless, shaking with fever under their leaky shelters. As in Russia, Napoleon waited too long. By the time he decided to recall the remnant of this grand army of conquest, yellow fever had claimed 22,000 of his warriors—the Negroes had killed only a few hundred.

The narrow strip of land (10 miles wide and about 50 miles long) known as the Canal Zone separates the two great oceans of the world—the Atlantic and the Pacific. It is a causeway only 9° north of the equator. The pride of the United States' possessions in the tropics, it is today one of the healthiest spots in the world.

Fifty years ago, however, it was a different story. Cursed by a deadly climate, narcotized by a sweltering heat, this stretch of land was once a pestilential jungle. Previously a den of thieves and murderers, and possessing the most colossal grave-yard of yellow fever victims anywhere in the world, nevertheless it was to become an arena of ineffable courage, daring, and adventure.

Across this isthmus once flowed all the looted riches of Peru. Carried by ships to Panama, the fabulous treasures were taken by pack mule trains over the "gold road," a jungle trail to Cruces, on the Atlantic side. From there the precious loot was shipped by waiting fleets to fill the coffers of Spain.

The rugged trail today is studded with dead men's bones, grim remains of the yellow plague. The early adventurers who attempted to settle there died by the thousands. Enrique de Guzman, the historian, in 1545 estimated that, of every 100 persons who set foot on this neck of land, 40 died of the fever. The total number of Spaniards who paid this price is unknown, but historians believe that the number greatly exceeds 25,000.

When the wealth of Peru was finally exhausted and the flow of travel ceased, the gold road was gradually reclaimed by the jungle. But not for long. In a few centuries the lure of the yellow metal once again beckoned to other travelers.

Then came the discovery of gold in California in 1848. Thousands of Americans hitched up for the fabled Eldorado. To avoid the long, dangerous continental journey, they sought this shorter trail across the Panamanian isthmus, blazed 300 years earlier by the Spanish explorers. The entire distance had to be made on foot through this dread jungle, steaming with vapor and lush with vegetation and hanging vines which blocked every foot of the way.

Day after day the weary travelers struggled on. Only a few miles were covered each day. At night, weary and hungry, they threw themselves on the ground. But no sleep came to them. The mosquitoes which had tortured them during the day finished them off at night. Each morning found fewer able to continue. Many who finally reached the Pacific side never touched the soil of California. They died in Panama, their

eyes glowing with fever and golden visions of a land they
never reached.

And so the years passed. Unable to conquer yellow fever,
man had to live with it, suffer and die from it. In 1880, after
the canal across the isthmus had aroused intense interest, a
French Canal Company was organized to attempt its construction. It was obvious from the start that this gigantic under-
taking would present an unparalleled engineering problem.
Staggering as it was, it proved to be no greater than the fear of
yellow fever. Where could the Canal Company turn to recruit
labor for this staggering job?

The first workers came from France. The men had hardly
settled in their quarters before they came down with the fever.
Before the second contingent could arrive, most of the first ar-
rivals had perished. Undaunted, the French looked to Ireland,
China, India, and the West Indies for more laborers. They
came—but they had no better luck. Between 1880 and 1886,
over 30,000 had died and thousands of others were suffering
from the terrible pestilence. Construction work crawled along
at a snail's pace. Yellow fever was winning another victory.

Broken by heavy financial losses, with less than one fifth
of the job completed and tortured by a seemingly unconquer-
able enemy, the French Canal Company finally abandoned its
canal adventure and returned to France.

People sometimes attempt to justify calamities by pointing
to the good that eventually comes from them. On such grounds,
even wars can scarcely be justified. Surely progress is not necessarily founded on calamity alone. One can only say that it is
a sad comment on mankind.

The Spanish-American war might have been justified. It not
only brought freedom to the nations under the medieval yoke
of Spain, it also made possible the completion of the Panama
Canal and the opening of a new world of trade. But its chief
contribution to human welfare was immensely more important
than these. This war inspired a new effort in our battle on the
microbe. As a direct result, one of the world's most persistent
medical enigmas was solved. In a highly dramatic setting, the

mosquito *Stegomyia* was named carrier of the yellow fever virus.

When the Spanish-American war ended, many American troops in Cuba were found to be infected with yellow fever. With a hopeful eye on the abandoned Panama Canal, the United States Government sent a commission to the island to see what could be done. This commission, consisting of Major Walter Reed, Dr. Jesse Lazear, Dr. James Carroll, and Dr. Aristedes Agromonte, arrived in Cuba in 1900.

The thrilling events that followed have been immortalized by Hollywood in the dramatic film "Yellow Jack." But to the men in Cuba it was an appalling epic of filth. Yellow fever was believed to be spread through contact with infected victims, especially through their clothing. This belief was almost universal. However, a Cuban physician, Dr. Carlos Finlay, had advanced it as his personal belief, based upon keen observation, that the disease was spread by the bite of mosquitoes.

The commission was confronted with two specific theories which needed investigation.

Starting with Finlay's idea, the Americans began experimenting with the mosquito. In order to ensure perfect control, tests were carried out with "home-grown" insects. Hungry mosquitoes were hatched from eggs supplied by the Cuban doctor. They were allowed to jab the flesh of yellow fever patients and suck their blood. Then these insects were recaged. After a few days, when they were starved, they were allowed to bite healthy individuals. One of these was Dr. Finlay himself.

Soon exciting things began to happen. Four days after he was bitten, Dr. Finlay came down with yellow fever, barely escaping death.

Another scientist bitten by an infected mosquito was not so lucky. A few days after Dr. Lazear had entertained one of these insects by permitting her to feed on blood from the back of his hand, he became violently ill. In spite of all that his colleagues could do to save him, he died of yellow fever. The third, Dr. Carroll, likewise developed the disease from a similar source but, with better luck than Lazear, he recovered.

Not since Pasteur's demonstration in 1881 of the effect of the anthrax bacilli at Melun, France, did the world watch a piece of scientific investigation with such fascination. There was little doubt now that Finlay was right.

It was in the early fall of 1900. In November the scientists established an experimental station in honor of their colleague, Dr. Lazear, and called for volunteers from among the American soldiers of occupation. The ready response of these men, who refused any reward or special consideration, knowing that they were facing death, constitutes a special chapter in the annals of human bravery.

For weeks the doctors inoculated volunteers with infected mosquitoes. All this served only to strengthen this thesis: susceptible human victims exposed to the bite of infected *Stegomyia* promptly developed yellow fever. The mosquito was, beyond doubt, at least one of the spreaders of the disease.

But this discovery completed only one side of the picture. The other side was this: Does close contact with the soiled clothing of a yellow fever victim also spread the disease? Obviously, there was only one way to find out. Do some testing.

A one-room, insect-proof house was especially built and artificially heated. The temperature was kept continuously above 32° Centigrade—the atmosphere most adaptable for the inducement of yellow fever. Sheets and pillow cases, all freshly removed from the beds of deceased victims and soiled with their blood, perspiration, urine, feces, and vomit, were brought into the room. The heat was stifling, the stench unbearable. Then the men were brought in. Every night for 3 weeks 3 volunteers slept in this miserable room.

One group after another was subjected to this routine. With each group the results were the same. *No one contracted yellow fever*. In a few months science had solved a mystery which had baffled men for many years. Yellow fever was spread only by the *Stegomyia* mosquito. The names of Major Walter Reed and his associates, conquerors of yellow fever, surely must be added to those who occupy a special place in medical history. Their epic achievement stands as an inspiration in the long battle against disease.

～～ 13 ～～

Global War on the Microbe

So we see that man is gradually winning his battle against the microbe. But many medical emergencies can arise—and still do.

One day in the summer of 1947 a man boarded a bus in Mexico City and, after several stops across the continent, arrived in New York City. Feeling slightly ill, he visited a physician who sent him to Bellevue Hospital, which in turn sent him to the Willard Parker Hospital for observation. Three weeks later the man died of smallpox and set in motion the greatest civilian vaccination project in all history.

Within a month 6 million people had been vaccinated to fight the dread smallpox virus. The facilities of city, state, and Federal agencies were harnessed in the drive. Long lines waited outside hospitals, health centers, and police stations. People walked the streets of New York City with one arm bared, waiting for their vaccinations to dry. Private physicians were placed on the city payroll in the emergency to speed the work. Fighting a possible epidemic, the city went "scratch" crazy, and the first question on people's lips when they met was, "Have you had your scratch yet?"

The man who perhaps did most to mobilize the medical

Fighting a possible smallpox epidemic in New York in 1947, the city went "scratch crazy."

forces in this unprecedented campaign was the city's commissioner of health, Dr. Israel Weinstein. He received confirmation of the smallpox diagnosis from the Army's laboratory in Washington, D. C., about noon on Good Friday. Within a few hours the entire Health Department staff, including this writer, had swung into action. The Department was put on emergency schedule. The staff slept very little that month, but only two deaths from smallpox occurred in the entire city.

The honor for having started this whole affair belongs to Edward Jenner, the eminent surgeon of Gloucestershire, England. Jenner is generally regarded as the father of vaccination. The outstanding medical triumph of the closing years of the eighteenth century was his confirmation of this striking biological phenomenon: when the body overcomes certain contagious diseases, it develops lifelong resistance to them. Upon this knowledge was founded the now universal practice of vaccination.

Jenner, of course, was not the first to make use of inoculation. Long before, the Turks had employed a similar form of immunization against smallpox. When Lady Mary Montague returned to England from the East, she told the story of this Turkish practice. It was also known that an East Indian tribe, as protection against injury by deadly snakes, swallowed small amounts of snake venom, which produced a resistance to the poison. Immunization had also been practiced in America as early as 1722 by Dr. Zabdiel Boylston. During a smallpox epidemic in Boston, he inoculated 280 persons against the disease. As a result, only six died.

Jenner noticed that the milkmaids who handled cattle in his village often suffered from cowpox sores. But they never developed smallpox, at that time a very prevalent disease. From this he reasoned that a close relationship between cowpox and smallpox existed. In the process of fighting the cowpox, their bodies had developed a natural resistance to smallpox.

Certain that he was on the right track, Jenner decided to put his belief to actual test. He performed his experiment on a willing subject, a boy named James Phipps, whose father had died of smallpox. When Jenner's foul plan became known, the whole countryside rose up against him. What was he trying to do, kill the boy? They threatened to shoot him if young Phipps suffered injury. However, Jenner coolly proceeded with his experiment.

Obtaining his material from a cowpox lesion, he inoculated James and waited. Then, after a few days, he again inoculated him, not with cowpox material but with virulent exudate from a smallpox patient. Angry crowds surrounded his house. Days passed, and the crowd waited. But young Phipps remained as healthy as ever. Eventually, it dawned on the people that their doctor had indeed performed an invaluable service to humanity. They murmured their apologies and went home. Thus did science come into its own in the little town of Gloucestershire.

Ever since microbe hunting began, bacteriologists have been kept busy answering questions. Two most often asked are: (1) How do some folks, in the midst of an epidemic, escape infection, while others, far less exposed, become easy victims? (2) How has man, surrounded for centuries by these hostile enemies, still managed to survive?

So many factors are involved that a simple answer is impossible. One explanation is that persons who escape an infection, though exposed to the germs, escape not so much because of luck but because of a far more important factor—they possess a natural immunity against that particular disease.

All human beings are endowed with a biological heritage. This heritage is their fortification against certain contagious diseases. Though they might serve as a reservoir for disease germs and transmit them to others, they themselves never become victims.

This phenomenon finds a somewhat related parallel among the lower animals. Cows, for example, are not susceptible to typhoid fever, diphtheria, or gonococcus. Yet they frequently are the victims of tuberculosis, spotted fever, and foot-and-mouth disease. Sheep do not die of smallpox or of scarlet fever but they often die of cholera and anthrax.

Because of the pernicious nature of the microbe, nature has

wisely endowed the human organism with a double defense system. The outer defenses are the mucous membrane and the skin, which serve as an effective barrier against pathogenic microorganisms seeking entrance into our system.

Despite the efficiency of this outer line of defense, deadly microbes occasionally gain entrance. Whenever this occurs, the invaders soon find themselves confronted by several internal obstacles. The first of these are two separate groups of cells. The macrophages, or wandering cells, make short work of the invaders by completely engulfing them. The other group, the leukocytes, or white cells, perform a slightly different but similar function. In addition to these cannibal cells, many internal glands secrete fluids so antiseptic that few microbes are able to survive them. Only by escaping these dangers can the germs survive. If they are of sufficient virulence, they will multiply rapidly and cause disease.

Despite Jenner's success, the cause of smallpox remained unknown. Though many must have thought of it, no one formulated a theory of its etiology.

With no foundation theory of vaccination to work on, Louis Pasteur, in 1880, came forward with this idea: the vaccine had carried the disease to young Phipps in a greatly weakened or attenuated form—enough to induce a mild illness but not enough to produce the disease. In striving to overcome this shock, the body had built up a resistance to even a full dose of virulent organisms. But Pasteur did not stop here. Why should the principle which worked so admirably with smallpox not work equally well with diphtheria, typhoid fever, or any other disease?

Pasteur at this time was trying to find a remedy for chicken cholera. Now he saw a good opportunity to test his theory. But before beginning his research, he was persuaded by his wife to take a short rest to gather new strength. Pasteur agreed, but instead of destroying his tubes of cholera cultures before leaving, he left them helter-skelter on his laboratory table.

Upon his return he injected some of these old cultures into

healthy chickens. To his surprise he found that they would no longer produce cholera in the chickens. Instead of killing them, the cultures merely made them droopy. Obviously, something unforeseen had happened. The virulence of the cultures had been lost.

Something even more startling was amiss. The chickens which were now injected with the old cultures would not develop cholera even when they received full doses of virulent microbes. Though this was decidedly a step toward his goal, Pasteur realized that it was hardly a discovery at all. It revealed little not previously suspected and was only a short step beyond what Jenner had demonstrated. The nature of the reaction in vaccine therapy remained a mystery, but Pasteur was determined to solve it.

The French cattle and sheep industry was taking a terrific beating. A deadly disease known as anthrax, first mentioned by Virgil, had made serious inroads among the animals, killing thousands and defying all efforts to help the miserable beasts.

Strangely enough, Robert Koch in 1880 had discovered the bacillus that causes anthrax. This discovery had contributed materially to the establishment of the germ theory of disease. But of what practical use was it? The poor animals were still dying. Yet, since it was possible to discover the cause of the disease, it should be possible also to find a remedy. And so, moved by the pleas of the leaders of the cattle industry, Pasteur tackled the problem.

His initial efforts resulted in dismal failure. The sheep and the cattle died in spite of his "immunity doses," followed by virulent cultures. Pasteur was perplexed. A fickle press shouted his failure as boldly as it had heralded his successes. Pasteur's luck is running out, his critics sneered.

But Pasteur was undismayed. He began growing anthrax bacteria in meat broth, heating the broth to a temperature high enough to deplete the microbes. Then he injected these depleted doses into the sheep. It made them sick, but they recovered. However, when he administered full doses of virulent anthrax bacilli the sheep developed anthrax and died.

Still, Pasteur was not willing to quit.

"I have no intention of giving up these experiments," he told his wife. "I will continue them and avoid my previous errors. Those full doses of the germs were too sudden and the depleted shots had not sufficiently prepared the animals for the sudden shock of the full doses."

So Pasteur began giving smaller injections of the depleted vaccines. When the beasts had overcome the first one, he gave a second and then a third dose, each succeeding dose larger than the one before. After the animals had recovered from the last dose, virulent cultures of anthrax bacilli were shot into their veins. After the fourth day, every one of the animals was still alive and healthy.

Pasteur had proved overwhelmingly that acquired immunity could be conferred upon an individual or an animal by means of vaccine therapy.

The use of drugs to cure disease had, indeed, made little progress until after the discovery of the cause of disease. This marked the beginning of a great effort by chemists and bacteriologists to find specific drugs for specific diseases. The formulation of the germ theory not only launched microbe hunting on a respectable career but also intensified the search for new drugs.

Lister had already successfully applied carbolic acid to infected wounds. But carbolic acid could not be used internally because of its destructive action on the body cells. Actually, neither Lister nor Pasteur knew how microbes could be killed internally. The Congress of Internal Medicine, which held its session in Wiesbaden in 1883, declared that "inner disinfection was impossible."

Here, indeed, was a staggering challenge to medicine. How could germs be killed without destroying the tissues?

One of those who took up the challenge was Paul Ehrlich. A brilliant chemist and biologist, he pioneered in the field of chemotherapy—the attempt to eradicate pathogenic microbes with drugs. With his famous "606" ("the magic bullet"), he was to win universal admiration and acclaim.

Early in his scientific career, Ehrlich became possessed with the idea of finding some drug that would prove to be disastrous to microbes without injury to man. It was his greatest dream, and he dedicated his life to it.

Intrigued by the work of the pathologist, Karl Weigert, Ehrlich started with dyes as the chemical compound which offered the most promising results. In order to study the cells of human tissues and the extent of the damage done to them by microbes, Weigert had made use of the microtome. This device sliced tissues thinner than ordinary paper. He had immersed them in dyes to color the cells for microscopic examination. Certain cells and germs showed an affinity for particular hues. Since dyes could stain microbes, Weigert concluded that there should be dyes to kill them.

Ehrlich was greatly inspired by Weigert. He would color microbes in living animals to bring about their destruction. Ehrlich never found the perfect dye, or the "magic bullet," as he called it, that would kill disease germs in the bodies of living animals with a single shot. However, by his pioneering researches he paved the way for the discovery of the sulfa drugs and penicillin more than 30 years after his death.

In 1885, Ehrlich began working with dyes to kill malaria parasites. Achieving no success in this field, he switched to the tubercle bacilli. As a result, he himself developed tuberculosis and was forced to seek the climate of Egypt to recover. Returning to Germany after an 18-month absence, he resumed his experiments, not with the tubercle bacilli but with other organisms.

At this time Laveran was working in the Pasteur Institute in Paris. He had done some research on the trypanosome microbe, the cause of African sleeping sickness. Now he used an arsenical compound which he found had a specific effect upon the organism. With both trypanosomes and some of the arsenic compound sent him by Laveran, Ehrlich had the ideal tools to start his work in chemotherapy.

So Ehrlich pressed his search for the magic bullet. After a great many experiments, which only stained the nerve cells of his mice and turned their ears pink, he found one, trypan red, that aroused his hopes. Injected into infected mice, it not only destroyed the trypanosomes in the animals, but also protected healthy ones against the development of the disease. However, when the compound was injected into rats and guinea pigs, it proved to be almost useless, causing several undesirable reactions in the animals. Ehrlich and his assistant, Shiga, tried over 500 dyes, but not one of these did the trick.

As with most men who dedicate their lives to a cause, they did not give up.

In 1904, Ehrlich turned to another arsenic compound called Atoxyl. This compound was created by the French chemist, Pierre Jacques Antoine Bechamp. It had been used previously on many South African natives by Robert Koch and others in an attempt to cure them of sleeping sickness. Though it had proved to be effective against the trypanosome microbes themselves, it was a failure on its human guinea pigs. Among other unpleasant reactions, it had caused total blindness.

Therefore, before making further use of Atoxyl to kill microbes, Ehrlich decided to change its chemical composition. Through this change he derived many other compounds. One of these, which he tried as his 606th experiment, in 1910, is the now famous 606, or salvarsan. It not only killed the trypanosome but also *Treponema pallidum*, the germ of syphilis, one of the original objects of his long and untiring quest.

Salvarsan, when properly administered, cured most cases of syphilis. But fatalities sometimes followed its administration. Effective in the earlier stages, it often proved to be useless after the disease had reached a more advanced stage. Another disadvantage was that prolonged treatments were required. Undaunted by only partial success, he continued his search for a perfect antisyphilitic remedy. He tested some 300 additional compounds and, as a result, gave the world many valuable drugs.

Ever since Ehrlich's attempts to cure syphilis with salvarsan, many others have tried to carry on this work. In battling these enemies of man through the ages, science has fought stubbornly and grimly. Finally, in 1935, came the break. In that year occurred the greatest medical triumph since Pasteur and Lister proved that microbes caused disease.

In Germany, in 1919, Dr. Gerhard Domagk, Director of the Institute of Experimental Pathology, embarked on the search for a drug to halt strep and other infections. After developing several related compounds, he produced a brick-red powder called Prontosil.

Injections of this drug into infected mice brought quick recovery. Here, apparently, was something new. The drug killed bacteria without inflicting any harm on the body. Domagk tested the drug on other animals with amazing results. All the animals recovered. The next step was, of course, to test it on human beings. For his first human subjects, he selected several patients who were near death—and once again he met with overwhelming success.

In Paris stands the famous Pasteur Institute, a bitter research rival of the German experimental group. An analysis of Prontosil at the Pasteur Institute revealed its hidden curative factor. It was sulfanilamide.

Here, at last, was a wonder drug—a magic bullet—to cure not only syphilis but also blood poisoning, pneumonia, childbed fever, and a score of other diseases. In November 1939, in recognition of Gerhard Domagk's outstanding contribution to medicine, he was offered the Nobel Prize; however, as a loyal citizen of the Third Reich, he firmly declined it.

Without doubt, Prontosil, the forerunner of the sulfonamide drugs, was the most important medical discovery since Ehrlich began his search for a magic bullet. Until 1942, its derivatives, the sulfa drugs, were the most deadly microbe killers known to medical science. They were the monarchs of drug therapy. In that year, however, penicillin, a powerful newcomer into the field, made its appearance.

As with many great discoveries, penicillin was an accident. Dr. Alexander Fleming, a British scientist of the St. Mary's Hospital Laboratory, in London, was engaged one morning in his usual bacterial researches. While making a routine examination of his culture plates for signs of contamination—those spots of microbes which have a habit of showing up on cultures where they are not wanted—he noticed something peculiar on one of his plates.

It was a growth of a colony of mold. This wasn't exactly unusual, since bacteriologists often find such undesirable growths in their cultures. Under ordinary circumstances, they are promptly discarded. However, the mold growth on this plate was behaving unlike anything Dr. Fleming had ever seen before. It was acting like a cannibal, devouring other microbe colonies which grew around it, thus leaving itself surrounded by a clear area.

Dr. Fleming transferred specimens of this unusual mold onto fresh culture plates to see whether or not the phenomenon would repeat itself. It did. He also noticed this difference: the mold was discriminating in the species of microbes it devoured. The colonies it ignored are known as gram-negative. They were so named because of their inability to absorb certain colored stains devised by the Danish bacteriologist, Hans Christian Joachim Gram. Another group, gram-positive, was readily destroyed by the mold.

Among the gram-positives are pathogenic bacteria, such as streptococcus, the pneumococcus, and the staphylococcus. Here then, Dr. Fleming found, was a species of mold which would destroy many of the common pathogens. Because of a lack of funds and adequate facilities, further research on this project was not carried out.

However, the advent of World War II created a new and intense interest in research. A frantic hunt began for new weapons to fight the microbe. Though the sulfa drugs had performed remarkably well, they were not infallible. There were even instances when they proved to be a great disappointment. Something better than the sulfa drugs to fight infection in war wounds was desperately needed.

At the time of his great discovery, Dr. Fleming made an interesting observation. Though penicillin was far more deadly to microbes than the sulfa drugs, this was demonstrated only in the test tube. How would it affect organisms which had already entered the human body? Would it stop their deadly work of blood and tissue disintegration?

Spurred by the needs of war, research on penicillin sped forward. Drs. Howard Florey and Ernst Chain at Oxford, and Karl Meyer and his associates at Columbia University, joined the hunt. It was now largely a matter of determining the specific element in the mold which had the cannibal habits. After it was found, there came the work of extracting and producing the known substance. The scientists extracted from it infinitesimally small amounts of a yellow powder. This was tested on mice inoculated with the dangerous strep and pneumo organisms, and the mice lived! Tests on people were equally convincing. Of the first 129 patients treated in a single hospital, 128 recovered.

Penicillin suddenly became the most wonderful of all drugs. It was potent not only against germs which caused pneumonia and blood poisoning but also against gonococcus infection, syphilis, meningitis, and other serious diseases. While Ehrlich searched tirelessly for the magic bullet to cure syphilis, Fleming succeeded—almost accidentally—a half century later.

It was surely the greatest discovery of our time.

New Hope for Tomorrow

Thus encouraged on many fronts, medicine began to leap forward with even greater strides.

The Christmas holidays had meant little to Mrs. Ingram that rainy afternoon in December 1943. Something bothered her. Her head throbbed frightfully, and her temperature was up slightly. On other occasions when she was feeling ill, she had simply gone to bed and tried to sleep it off. This time, however, she was certain that it was not going to be so easy. It wasn't.

Two days later she was in the hospital. Her case was diagnosed as undulant fever, and the doctors wondered where she had picked it up. If infection had occurred through unpasteurized milk, the usual channel, they were quite sure that the microbes were still on the rampage. Other victims would soon be coming in.

During the next few days, in spite of the best medical care, Mrs. Ingram became worse. Her doctors watched her gulp down dose after dose of sulfa drugs. When these failed to bring relief, they administered penicillin. But that, too, did no good.

A young interne offered a suggestion. He recalled the glowing radio and newspaper accounts of a newly discovered drug, an antibiotic called *streptomycin*. It had been discovered by a Rutgers University professor, and it blasted microbes that defied all other remedies. There were, for example, the 66 soldiers in a Canadian hospital suffering from urinary tract infections. Though defying the destroying might of the sulfa drugs and penicillin, they had promptly yielded to the new antibacterial wonder.

In Philadelphia doctors had labored to save the life of a man dying of a severe case of typhoid fever, but all their efforts had come to nought. However, a few injections of streptomycin into his veins halted the microbes and started the patient on his way to recovery.

From various Army hospitals, where the drug was undergoing clinical tests, streptomycin was apparently performing miracles. It was especially effective against that large group of gram-negative bacteria which had shown little or no positive response to other treatments. On many fronts streptomycin was soon producing dramatic results.

All of this had made wonderful newspaper copy. It was heartening news to the thousands of sufferers from these gram-negative bacilli. But how could all this benefit Mrs. Ingram, who was now dying of undulant fever? And how could the doctors get some of it? The total amount available in the entire world was less than 200 grams!

Forty-eight hours later, thanks to radio and persistent telephone appeals, Mrs. Ingram received some of the precious substance. In a short time she was on her way to recovery, a bottle dripping a cloudy streptomycin solution into her veins.

Though penicillin was called an accidental discovery, streptomycin came to us through arduous labor. Its discovery was the result of the specific planning of Dr. Selman A. Waksman, microbiologist at the New Jersey Experimental Station of Rutgers University. Behind it is another story of hope, of work, of frustration, and, finally, of triumph—the main ingredients of all human progress.

During the ages countless millions of people have succumbed

to bubonic plague, typhus fever, cholera, diphtheria, and influenza. Millions more have died of tuberculosis and of other contagious diseases. The question has often been raised: what was the ultimate fate of the microbe responsible for the death of those unfortunate souls?

To this challenging question there was no positive answer. Some speculated that these microbes, in some mysterious manner, find their way into the air and give rise to epidemics. Objectors reminded them that pathogenic germs, the cause of such disasters, require human protein for their survival. Failing to obtain an adequate supply of this essential food in the soil, they ultimately die of starvation. Such germs, they declared, once confined to the soil, probably underwent physical transformations, becoming identified with the great families of soil microbes. Or perhaps they are set upon by other germs, inhabitants of the soil, who quickly liquidate them.

These theories were not without a certain interest. But was there no way of determining the specific fate of pathogenic organisms buried with their human victims? Actually, there was.

In 1909 W. D. Frost, experimenting with the fate of typhoid bacteria confined to the soil, found that 93 per cent of them had vanished within a week. What had happened to these bacteria? Did other pathogens buried in the soil suffer a similar fate? Frost admitted frankly that he did not know. However, he thought it not unlikely that hostile "resident" microbes had made short work of these "newcomers."

Not until the 1930's was an authentic light thrown upon the subject. In 1932 the National Research Council, led by Dr. Waksman, determined to solve the mystery. The investigation quickly disspelled the old fear of disease epidemics brewing in the soil. Epidemics did not originate in the soil. Instead, the Council confirmed the belief of Frost that pathogenic microorganisms buried with their victims were quickly destroyed by other bacteria. Here, then, was a clue.

But Dr. Waksman had long suspected this type of bacterial warfare going on in the soil. Let us expand our research, he urged; let us study this invisible society of the soil. It was Pasteur's old idea which, unfortunately, had remained in the shadows for more than a half century. Some day, Pasteur had prophesied, microbes might be used to destroy other microbes in the human body. And so it came to pass.

It was essentially the discovery of Dr. Waksman that sent a host of research men on a lively adventure in antibiotics. Using microbes or their products to destroy microbial diseases in man was certainly an ingenious idea. Substantially, it is responsible for the discovery of the antibiotic drugs which, since that time, have continued to bring new hope and help to humanity.

Waksman's entrance into the field of antibiotics stemmed largely from two major developments. The first of these was the outbreak of war on the European Continent. This conflict, Dr. Waksman surmised, would eventually spread, and with its expansion create a subsequent demand for additional antibacterial weapons. A second reason was the discovery of tyrothricin, a soil microbial compound with marked antibacterial properties, by one of his former students, Dr. René J. Dubos, of the Rockefeller Institute for Medical Research.

Inspired by these events, Dr. Waksman and an associate, H. B. Woodruff, embarked in 1939 upon an antibiotic research program. This was the time the phenomenal sulfa drugs were making the headlines. Waksman and Woodruff succeeded during the next few years in isolating two powerful antibiotic products. The first of these was called actinomycin. Like tyrothricin, it was shelved later because of its high toxicity.

The two scientists then came up with streptothricin, which seemed to be highly successful. Animals inoculated with lethal doses of certain species of pathogens and later injected with streptothricin seemed to recover. But this apparent recovery was followed by unfavorable reactions. Many of the animals suffered from delayed action of the drug. While at first they seemed to benefit, later they died of its toxic effects.

With penicillin having proved its effectiveness only against gram-positive bacteria, and with the ever-pressing demands of war, the need for other antibacterial products became urgent. Accordingly, in 1943, Waksman set about anew on the twofold purpose of finding a weapon against the gram-negative bacteria, and one that would lay siege to the age-old enemy of man, tuberculosis.

The desire to wage an all-out offensive against tuberculosis was not original with Dr. Waksman. It had been the cherished hope of bacteriologists and chemists since the days of Robert Koch.

With another assistant, Albert Schatz, Dr. Waksman launched his ambitious project in June 1943. It was obvious to them from the beginning that this effort would take years. However, the scientists had scarcely begun the initial stage of their program when they spotted the microbe *Streptomyces griseus*. Waksman had known about this for a long time. But now he and Albert Schatz put it to work and from it isolated the now famous streptomycin.

The preliminary tests with streptomycin were surprisingly successful. Mice were injected with fatal doses of various species of gram-negative pathogens. Then they were given shots of streptomycin. They all stayed well. Then guinea pigs were inoculated with such virulent organisms as those causing tularemia, undulant fever, and typhoid fever. Equally phenomenal results were achieved.

Soon reports began pouring in from clinics and research laboratories everywhere. Streptomycin was fulfilling its initial promise. At the Mayo Clinic it had cured mice injected with tularemia, or rabbit fever; in Philadelphia it had cured Salmonella infection; in Boston it had proved itself to be effective against typhoid fever. The drug, it appeared, did not kill the germs outright. It simply held them in check and prevented their multiplication until the body could muster its own defense and gain an advantage.

Besides holding the microbes in check, it had other satisfactory assets. Notable among them was the fact that streptomycin was more easily produced commercially than was penicillin. Here was a lifesaver not just for a few but for many.

Streptomycin was specific against gram-negative microbes,

118 NEW HOPE FOR TOMORROW

the first of Dr. Waksman's two great objectives. But what of the second objective—an antibiotic that would successfully attack the dreaded tubercle bacilli?

Studying the effects of streptomycin on the tubercle bacilli in the test tube, Waksman and his colleagues found reasons to be hopeful. It was soon apparent to them that these organisms showed a decided sensitivity to the drug. But they knew that they had to be cautious. So many drugs, after raising high hopes, had turned out to be bitter disappointments. Would streptomycin follow this all-too-familiar pattern? Or would it, in a single stroke, fulfill Waksman's great dream?

So began the exciting period of testing the drug on animals and the arduous task of working out optimum doses.

Among the first to test streptomycin on laboratory animals were Drs. H. C. Hinshaw and W. H. Feldman. At their laboratories 12 guinea pigs were inoculated with lethal doses of tubercle bacilli. These should have promptly proved to be fatal. Eight of these animals received no further attention, but four of them were given streptomycin. The eight that received no shots rapidly developed tuberculosis and died; those receiving the drug showed no signs of the disease.

Other reports brought more good news. Drs. G. P. Youmans and J. C. McCarter, working with white Swiss mice, obtained spectacular results. G. E. Rockwell found that rabbits and guinea pigs inoculated with tubercle bacilli, followed by injections of streptomycin, lived longer and seemed to be healthier than the controls which received no treatment. From dozens of research workers came varying reports; but everywhere streptomycin had shown definite inhibitory effects on the human type of tuberculosis.

From experiments with animals to experiments with humans is only a short step. In a State Hospital in Georgia, a group of 523 patients, doomed by tuberculosis, were subjected to streptomycin therapy. At the end of their treatment, 106 were discharged as cured, and 190 had shown marked improvements. The others had also made some gains, but unfortunately their illness had advanced too far before the treatment was begun.

In a Minnesota hospital, 100 patients with tuberculosis were

NEW HOPE FOR TOMORROW

selected to receive streptomycin. Thirty-two had tuberculosis of the lungs, others had tuberculosis of bone and joints and of the urinary tract. Given six shots daily, the majority showed progress.

The Veterans Hospital also obtained encouraging results with streptomycin therapy. Along with their optimism, however, came a note of caution. After initial improvements in practically all the patients treated, 16 per cent of them began to show some regression even before the treatment was completed. Great care, it was obvious, had to be taken in the treatment.

Following the spectacular accounts of the drug in the newspapers, tuberculous patients everywhere began to clamor for it. The magic word "streptomycin" hung on every patient's lips. It revived their hopes and gave them renewed courage. In one large hospital, feeling that this was their golden opportunity, the patients took it upon themselves to launch a campaign fund. With the slogan "Streptomycin for Every T.B. Sufferer," they raised $2,000 among themselves, which the public soon boosted to over $100,000.

Every patient was willing to become a guinea pig to receive the treatment. But the doctors had other ideas. Streptomycin, they knew, was not for every T.B. patient. Some were too far gone to benefit—and streptomycin was still too expensive. It would be wiser, they felt, to concentrate on those who still had the slightest chance of recovery.

Despite the high hopes raised by streptomycin as a promising weapon against tuberculosis, it was not without fundamental limitations. These included its high toxic effects and the development of microbial resistance to it, or drug-fastness. While it has established itself as a potent weapon in our arsenal against various types of human tuberculosis, it is not a cure-all. As its discoverers themselves cautioned, it is definitely not a substitute for the conventional and surgical processes that have long been used in T.B.

Our ceaseless fight against this deadly and infectious disease is not over. In the last few years, however, medicine has made other solid gains. Two other powerful drugs have come to our aid: *isoniazid and para-aminosalicylic acid*, commonly called PAS. These three antibiotics used in combination have at last provided the punch to halt T.B. in its tracks. But we still have so much to do, so far to go to knock T.B. out forever. The ailment has not been licked by any means.

. . . And so the struggle against the microbe proceeds unabated. The unsung heroes of medical research continue to delve, with painstaking care, into the mysteries of the microbe. Many new antibiotics are constantly being developed. We now have the Salk vaccine to fight crippling polio, and the Sabin and Cox live-virus vaccines that can be taken orally instead of by injection. Indeed, many scientists see these as even more powerful weapons in our great onslaught on polio. Surely we are gaining everywhere . . .

Thus our story for the moment comes to an end. But the fight goes on everywhere. Let us rejoice that in our unceasing battle against the tiny killers of mankind we are winning more and more victories. Certainly, on many fronts, we have fought well and are routing the enemy, despite the enormous obstacles still arrayed against us.

"Science is built up of facts, as a house is built up of stones," declared Lucien Poincaré in *Science and Hypothesis*, "but an accumulation of facts is no more science than a heap of stones is a house." Here is something to think about.

Surely we must build our house well, and build our science soundly. We must do it with courage and with kindness, with wisdom and vision, with a real love for all people, and a grim determination to forge ahead. Let us then hope that we will win out. Let us then hope that we will wipe the bloody slate dry.

Instead of fighting each other, let us hope that the nations will join together to fight their common enemies—disease and poverty and human sorrow. And if they do, surely we will find greater joy and richness in our lives and in the lives of all of God's children.

And let us anticipate that some day there will be no more plagues left to fight. Until that day, then, let us hope that we have the medical fighters to do the job.

Bibliography

Many medical books, journals, and pamphlets were consulted, among them copies of *World Health*, published bimonthly by the World Health Organization; *Health News*, published monthly by the New York State Department of Health; and *Health Bulletin*, published quarterly by the New York City Department of Health. Additional sources of information include:

1. Gordon, Maurice, M.D.: Medicine Among the Ancient Hebrews, History of Science Society, Inc., official journal, *Isis*, vol. 33, 1941.
2. Haggard, Howard W., M.D.: Devils, Drugs and Doctors, New York, Harper & Brothers, 1929.
3. Silverman, Milton: Magic in a Bottle, New York, Macmillan, 1948.
4. De Kruif, Paul: Microbe Hunters, New York, Harcourt, Brace, 1926.
5. Zinsser, Hans: Rats, Lice and History, Boston, Little, Brown, 1945.
6. Schatz, Albert, and Reidman, Sarah R.: Story of Microbes, New York, Harper & Brothers, 1952.
7. Major, Ralph H., M.D.: Disease and Destiny, New York, Appleton-Century, 1936.

Index